Foundation Mathematics for GCSE:

Chapter 1

■■■ Homework 1A

1 a 45 **b** 36 **c** 41 **d** 40 **e** 36
2 a 4, 2, 3 **b** 1, 2, 0, 3 **c** 7, 6, 1, 3, 41 **d** 6, 2, 7, 1, 12, 14 **e** 1, 6, 7, 4, 11, 5, 8, 36

■■■ Homework 1B

1 a 12 **b** 28 **c** 30 **d** 24 **e** 48 **f** 36 **g** 45 **h** 63 **i** 64 **j** 72 **k** 42 **l** 49 **m** 24 **n** 56 **o** 25
2 a 7 **b** 7 **c** 4 **d** 4 **e** 6 **f** 7 **g** 9 **h** 8 **i** 3 **j** 3 **k** 7 **l** 5 **m** 2 **n** 7 **o** 8
3 a 13 **b** 14 **c** 20 **d** 4 **e** 6 **f** 5 **g** 24 **h** 35 **i** 21 **j** 6 **k** 9 **l** 27 **m** 6 **n** 54 **o** 15
4 a 40 **b** 70 **c** 90 **d** 110 **e** 300 **f** 500 **g** 2400 **h** 4500 **i** 8 **j** 13 **k** 51 **l** 100 **m** 7 **n** 9
o 12

■■■ Homework 1C

1 a 19 **b** 16 **c** 8 **d** 6 **e** 6 **f** 12 **g** 11 **h** 2 **i** 6 **j** 20
2 a 18 **b** 2 **c** 2 **d** 9 **e** 9 **f** 13 **g** 4 **h** 20 **i** 15 **j** 4
3 a $4 \times (5 - 1)$ **b** $(8 \div 2) + 4$ **c** $(8 - 3) \times 4$ **d** $12 - (5 \times 2)$ **e** $3 \times (3 + 2)$ **f** $12 \div (2 + 1)$ **g** $9 \times (6 \div 3)$
h $20 - (8 + 5)$ **i** $(6 + 4) \div 2$ **j** $16 \div (4 \div 2)$
4 a $2 \times 5 - 10$ **b** $10 \div (2 \times 5)$ **c** $10 - (5 + 2)$ **d** $10 \times 2 \div 5$ **e** $(10 - 5) + 2$ **f** $5 + 10 \div 2$ **g** $10 + (5 - 2)$
h $5 + 10 + 2$ **i** $10 + 2 \times 5$ **j** $5 \times 10 \div 2$
5 $(3 + 4) \times 5 = 35$ and $3 + (4 \times 5) = 23$

■■■ Homework 1D

1 a 70 **b** 4 **c** 600 **d** 4 000 **e** 7 **f** 600 **g** 2 **h** 2000 **i** 80 000 **j** 7 000 000
2 a Seven thousand, two hundred and forty five **b** Nine thousand and seventy two
c Twenty nine thousand, four hundred and fifty **d** Two million, seven hundred and sixty thousand
3 a 8 500 **b** 42 042 **c** 6 000 000 **d** 5 000 005
4 a 8, 12, 14, 20, 22, 25, 30, 31 **b** 151, 155, 159, 167, 168, 170, 172, 176 **c** 1990, 1998, 2000, 2002, 2010, 2070, 2092, 2100
5 a 75, 72, 62, 57, 50, 49 **b** 1052, 1010, 1007, 999, 988, 980 **c** 4765, 4756, 4675, 4657, 4576, 4567
6 a 789, 798, 879, 897, 978, 987 **b** 789 **c** 987
7 66, 64, 62, 46, 44, 42, 26, 24, 22
8 a Twelve thousand, seven hundred and fifty six **b** Two hundred and thirty eight thousand
c Ninety four million, six hundred thousand

■■■ Homework 1E

1 a 30 **b** 70 **c** 20 **d** 50 **e** 60 **f** 10 **g** 100 **h** 120 **i** 110 **j** 130
2 a 200 **b** 400 **c** 400 **d** 800 **e** 900 **f** 100 **g** 600 **h** 300 **i** 1000 **j** 1200
3 a 2000 **b** 4000 **c** 7000 **d** 4000 **e** 1000 **f** 7000 **g** 6000 **h** 9000 **i** 2000 **j** 10 000
4 a 15 **b** 30 **c** 35 **d** 40 **e** 25 **f** 20
5 £8 000, £13 000, £45 000, £76 000, £100 000 **6 a** £235 **b** £245 or £244.99 **7 a** 7500 **b** 8500 or 8499

■■■ Homework 1F

1 a 98 **b** 401 **c** 600 **d** 8109 **e** 4917 **2 a** 126 **b** 642 **c** 933 **d** 985 **e** 5044
3 a 234 **b** 523 **c** 578 **d** 272 **e** 2853 **4 a** 90 **b** 191 **c** 66 **d** 542 **e** 5644
5 a 2, 7 **b** 4, 5 **c** 5, 6, 0 **d** 2, 6, 8 **6 a** 2, 6 **b** 6, 4 **c** 4, 4, 8 **d** 6, 2, 2

■■■ Homework 1G

1 a 72 **b** 152 **c** 620 **d** 2448 **e** 2872 **2 a** 105 **b** 259 **c** 1827 **d** 3504 **e** 19284
3 a 385 **b** £1.61 **c** 720 **d** £2272 **e** 10 560 **4 a** 342 **b** 175 **c** 201 **d** 1452 **e** 320
5 a 36 **b** 63 **c** 125 **d** £515 **e** 342

Chapter 2

■■■ Homework 2A

1 a $\frac{3}{4}$ **b** $\frac{2}{3}$ **c** $\frac{4}{5}$ **d** $\frac{3}{8}$ **e** $\frac{4}{9}$ **f** $\frac{5}{6}$ **g** $\frac{7}{10}$ **h** $\frac{7}{12}$
2 Diagrams drawn to show **a** $\frac{1}{3}$ **b** $\frac{3}{5}$ **c** $\frac{7}{10}$ **d** $\frac{5}{8}$ **e** $\frac{7}{9}$ **f** $\frac{3}{7}$ **g** $\frac{5}{12}$ **h** $\frac{7}{15}$

■■■ Homework 2B

1 a $\frac{2}{4}$ or $\frac{1}{2}$ **b** $\frac{3}{5}$ **c** $\frac{5}{7}$ **d** $\frac{6}{8}$ or $\frac{3}{4}$ **e** $\frac{5}{6}$ **f** $\frac{8}{9}$ **g** $\frac{7}{10}$ **h** $\frac{4}{5}$ **i** $\frac{5}{12}$ **j** $\frac{12}{20}$ or $\frac{3}{5}$

2 a $\frac{2}{5}$ **b** $\frac{4}{8}$ or $\frac{1}{2}$ **c** $\frac{4}{7}$ **d** $\frac{5}{10}$ or $\frac{1}{2}$ **e** $\frac{2}{6}$ or $\frac{1}{3}$ **f** $\frac{4}{9}$ **g** $\frac{6}{8}$ or $\frac{3}{4}$ **h** $\frac{2}{9}$ **i** $\frac{2}{12}$ or $\frac{1}{6}$ **j** $\frac{8}{20}$ or $\frac{2}{5}$
3 c i $\frac{5}{8}$ **ii** $\frac{7}{8}$ **iii** $\frac{3}{8}$ **iv** $\frac{7}{8}$ **v** $\frac{3}{8}$ **vi** $\frac{1}{8}$ **vii** $\frac{1}{8}$ **viii** $\frac{5}{8}$

▬ Homework 2C

1 a $\frac{5}{10}$ **b** $\frac{2}{10}$ **c** $\frac{4}{10}$ **d** $\frac{6}{10}$ **e** $\frac{8}{10}$ **2 a** $\frac{7}{10}$ **b** $\frac{8}{10}$ **c** $\frac{5}{10}$ **d** $\frac{9}{10}$ **e** $\frac{1}{10}$ **f** $\frac{3}{10}$
3 a $\frac{6}{12}$ **b** $\frac{3}{12}$ **c** $\frac{4}{12}$ **d** $\frac{9}{12}$ **e** $\frac{8}{12}$ **4 a** $\frac{10}{12}$ **b** $\frac{7}{12}$ **c** $\frac{11}{12}$ **d** $\frac{10}{12}$ **e** $\frac{11}{12}$ **f** $\frac{2}{12}$ **g** $\frac{5}{12}$ **h** $\frac{5}{12}$ **i** $\frac{4}{12}$ **j** $\frac{1}{12}$

▬ Homework 2D

1 a $\frac{3}{20}$ **b** $\frac{12}{20}$ **c** $\frac{10}{16}$ **d** $\frac{12}{16}$ **e** $\frac{10}{15}$ **f** $\frac{10}{18}$ **g** $\frac{30}{35}$ **h** $\frac{4}{40}$
2 a $\frac{3}{12} = \frac{4}{16} = \frac{5}{20}$ **b** $\frac{6}{9} = \frac{8}{12} = \frac{10}{15}$ **c** $\frac{8}{10} = \frac{12}{15} = \frac{16}{20} = \frac{20}{25} = \frac{24}{30}$ **d** $\frac{6}{10} = \frac{9}{30} = \frac{12}{40} = \frac{15}{50} = \frac{18}{60}$
3 a $\frac{3}{4}$ **b** $\frac{3}{4}$ **c** $\frac{3}{5}$ **d** $\frac{3}{4}$ **4 a** $\frac{2}{5}$ **b** $\frac{1}{4}$ **c** $\frac{1}{5}$ **d** $\frac{2}{5}$ **e** $\frac{2}{3}$ **f** $\frac{1}{3}$ **g** $\frac{3}{5}$ **h** $\frac{2}{3}$ **i** $\frac{3}{5}$ **j** $\frac{6}{7}$
5 a $\frac{1}{4}, \frac{1}{3}, \frac{1}{2}$ **b** $\frac{3}{8}, \frac{1}{2}, \frac{3}{4}$ **c** $\frac{7}{12}, \frac{2}{3}, \frac{5}{6}$ **d** $\frac{1}{4}, \frac{3}{10}, \frac{2}{5}$

▬ Homework 2E

1 a $2\frac{1}{2}$ **b** $1\frac{2}{3}$ **c** $1\frac{1}{4}$ **d** $3\frac{2}{3}$ **e** $4\frac{1}{2}$ **f** $3\frac{3}{4}$ **g** $2\frac{2}{5}$ **h** $2\frac{1}{2}$ **i** $2\frac{1}{3}$ **j** $2\frac{1}{8}$ **k** $1\frac{7}{10}$ **l** $3\frac{1}{4}$ **m** 3 **n** 4 **o** 6
2 a $\frac{3}{2}$ **b** $\frac{9}{4}$ **c** $\frac{7}{3}$ **d** $\frac{9}{2}$ **e** $\frac{11}{3}$ **f** $\frac{7}{4}$ **g** $\frac{11}{5}$ **h** $\frac{19}{8}$ **i** $\frac{17}{5}$ **j** $\frac{23}{8}$ **k** $\frac{43}{8}$ **l** $\frac{31}{7}$ **m** $\frac{49}{9}$ **n** $\frac{53}{12}$ **o** $\frac{77}{10}$

▬ Homework 2F

1 a $\frac{1}{2}$ **b** $\frac{4}{5}$ **c** $\frac{1}{2}$ **d** $\frac{2}{3}$ **e** $\frac{3}{5}$ **2 a** $1\frac{1}{2}$ **b** $1\frac{1}{2}$ **c** 1 **d** $1\frac{1}{3}$ **e** $1\frac{1}{5}$
3 a $\frac{5}{6}$ **b** $\frac{7}{10}$ **c** $\frac{2}{3}$ **d** $\frac{17}{20}$ **e** $1\frac{5}{12}$ **f** $1\frac{1}{3}$ **g** $3\frac{3}{4}$ **h** $4\frac{1}{12}$
4 a $\frac{1}{2}$ **b** $\frac{2}{5}$ **c** $\frac{1}{6}$ **d** $\frac{1}{6}$ **e** $\frac{7}{10}$ **f** $\frac{2}{5}$ **g** $1\frac{3}{4}$ **h** $3\frac{5}{12}$

▬ Homework 2G

1 $\frac{1}{10}$ **2** $\frac{8}{9}$ **3** $\frac{5}{12}$ **4** $\frac{5}{12}$ **5** $\frac{7}{20}$ **6** $\frac{2}{15}$

▬ Homework 2H

1 a 10 **b** 12 **c** 6 **d** 30 **e** 10 **f** 6 **g** 6 **h** 35
2 a £200 **b** 40 kg **c** 150 m **d** 18 g **e** 24 mins **f** 84 m
3 a 15 **b** 10 **c** 9 **d** 45 **4** 16 **5** £48 **6** 10 hours **7 a** 12 cm **b** 52 cm **8 a** £160 **b** £640

▬ Homework 2I

1 a $\frac{1}{4}$ **b** $\frac{3}{4}$ **c** $\frac{3}{5}$ **d** $\frac{4}{7}$ **e** $\frac{1}{3}$ **f** $\frac{1}{8}$ **2** $\frac{1}{6}$ **3** $\frac{3}{8}$ **4 a** $\frac{4}{5}$ **b** $\frac{1}{5}$

▬ Homework 2J

1 $\frac{1}{4}$ **2** $\frac{1}{15}$ **3** $\frac{1}{12}$ **4** $\frac{3}{8}$ **5** $\frac{3}{15}$ **6** $\frac{1}{3}$ **7** $\frac{2}{5}$ **8** $\frac{1}{6}$ **9** $\frac{1}{4}$ **10** $\frac{1}{4}$

Chapter 3

▬ Homework 3A

1 −£20 **2** profit **3** −500 m **4** above **5** −7 °C **6** −1 °C **7** above 8 **8** North **9** −10 mph **10** − 3

▬ Homework 3B

1 and 2   Many different answers to each part
3 a < **b** > **c** < **d** < **e** < **f** < **g** < **h** > **i** > **j** >
4 a

| −10 | −8 | −6 | −4 | −2 | 0 | 2 | 4 | 6 | 8 | 10 |

b

| −25 | −20 | −15 | −10 | −5 | 0 | 5 | 10 | 15 | 20 | 25 |

c

| −50 | −40 | −30 | −20 | −10 | 0 | 10 | 20 | 30 | 40 | 50 |

d

| −500 | −400 | −300 | −200 | −100 | 0 | 100 | 200 | 300 | 400 | 500 |

e

| −125 | −100 | −75 | −50 | −25 | 0 | 25 | 50 | 75 | 100 | 125 |

▬ Homework 3C

1 a 3 **b** 2 **c** 1 **d** 4 **e** 2 **f** 5 **g** 0 **h** 0 **i** −1 **j** −2 **k** −4 **l** −4 **m** −2 **n** −1 **o** −4
p −2 **q** −9 **r** −6 **s** −10 **t** −10
2 a −4 **b** −14 **c** −12 **d** −5 **e** −6 **f** −10 **g** −22 **h** −35 **i** −7
3 a −1 **b** 2 **c** −7 **d** −4 **e** 3 **f** 6 **g** 0 **h** −8 **i** −10

Homework 3D

1 a −3 **b** 9 **c** −2 **d** 10 **e** −8 **f** −7 **g** 3 **h** −6 **i** 0
2 a −18 **b** −20 **c** −19 **d** −8 **e** 28 **f** 21 **g** −19 **h** −20 **i** −21 **j** −28
3 a 4 °C **b** 0 °C **c** −1 °C **d** −3 °C **e** −7 °C
4 a 2 °C **b** 6 °C **c** 3 °C **5 a** −6, −5, −3, −1, 1, 2, 3, 8 **b** −12, −10, −8, −5, 0, 4, 5, 6
6 a 3, 8 **b** −6, −1 **c** −6, 11 **d** 3, 2 **e** −3, 3

Homework 3E

1 a −2, −4, −6 **b** −4, −7, −10 **c** 0, 5, 10 **d** 0, −5, −11 **e** −6, −4½, −3 **2** 8 °C **3 a** 6 °C **b** 15 °C
4 a Athens **b** Beijing, 41 °C **c** Nairobi, 18 °C **5** 7, −1, −4, 3, −5

Chapter 4

Homework 4A

1 a 4, 8, 12, 16, 20 **b** 6, 12, 18, 24, 30 **c** 8, 16, 24, 32, 40 **d** 12, 24, 36, 48, 60 **e** 15, 30, 45, 60, 75
2 a 28, 36, 64, 56, 60 **b** 15, 45 **c** 64, 56 **d** 77, 66
3 a 252, 161, 224, 378, 315, 182 **b** 225, 252, 297, 162, 378, 315, 369 **c** 252, 312
4 a 198 **b** 196 **c** 195 **d** 192 **e** 198 **5 a** 12 **b** 102 **c** 1002 **d** 10 002 **e** 1 000 000 002

Homework 4B

1 a 1, 2, 3, 4, 6, 12 **b** 1, 13 **c** 1, 3, 5, 15 **d** 1, 2, 4, 5, 10, 20 **e** 1, 2, 11, 22 **f** 1, 2, 3, 4, 6, 9, 12, 18, 36
g 1, 2, 3, 6, 7, 14, 21, 42 **h** 1, 2, 3, 4, 6, 8, 12, 16, 24, 48 **i** 1, 7, 49 **j** 1, 2, 5, 10, 25, 50
2 a 1, 2, 4, 5, 10, 20, 25, 50, 100 **b** 1, 3, 37, 111 **c** 1, 5, 25, 125 **d** 1, 2, 3, 4, 6, 11, 12, 22, 33, 44, 66, 132
e 1, 2, 4, 5, 7, 10, 14, 20, 28, 35, 70, 140
3 a 13 **b** 23 **c** 25 **d** 33 **e** 42 **f** 44 **g** 51 **h** 53 **i** 72 **j** 81 The answer is the two outer digits of the number

Homework 4C

1 2, 3, 5, 7, 11, 13, 17, 19, 23, 29, 31, 37 **2** 43, 47, 59, 61, 67
3 a $2 \times 2 \times 2 \times 2 - 1 = 15$, $2 \times 2 \times 2 \times 2 \times 2 - 1 = 31$, $2 \times 2 \times 2 \times 2 \times 2 \times 2 - 1 = 63$ **b** Lines 2, 3 and 5
4 1, 4, 9, 16, 25, 36, 49, 64, 81, 100 **5 a** $5 \times 3 + 1 = 16$, $6 \times 4 + 1 = 25$, $7 \times 5 + 1 = 36$ **b** They are square numbers
6 a 25 **b** 225 **c** 625 **d** 1225 **e** 2025 **f** 3025 **g** 4225 **h** 5625 **i** 7225 **j** 9025 Answers all end in 25

Homework 4D

1 a 8 **b** 5 **c** 7 **d** 9 **e** 4 **f** 6 **g** 10 **h** 11 **i** 12 **j** 20
2 a 15 **b** 17 **c** 21 **d** 25 **e** 33 **f** 37 **g** 56 **h** 78 **i** 202 **j** 333
3 a $\sqrt{1} + \sqrt{4} + \sqrt{9} + \sqrt{16} = 10$, $\sqrt{1} + \sqrt{4} + \sqrt{9} + \sqrt{16} + \sqrt{25} = 15$, $\sqrt{1} + \sqrt{4} + \sqrt{9} + \sqrt{16} + \sqrt{25} + \sqrt{36} = 21$
b The answers are triangle numbers

Homework 4E

1 a 8 **b** 64 **c** 343 **d** 1000 **e** 1728 **f** 81 **g** 10 000 **h** 32 **i** 1 000 000 **j** 256
2 a 121 **b** 1331 **c** 14 641
First and the last digit is 1 and the numbers are palindromic but are not palindromic for other powers
3 a 7, 14, 21, 28, 35 **b** 1, 2, 3, 5, 6, 10, 15, 30 **c** 2, 3, 5, 7, 11, 13, 17, 19, 23, 29, 31 **d** 36 **e** 5 **f** 27

Chapter 5

Homework 5A

1 a 20 cm **b** 18 cm **c** 36 cm **d** 18 cm **e** 32 cm **f** 36 cm **2** Examples of rectangles with perimeters of 14 cm
3 Yes, use fractions of a cm, e.g. a rectangle 2 cm by 2.5 cm

Homework 5B

1 a 6 **b** 13 **c** 4½ **d** 5 **2 a** 9–11 **b** 12–14 **c** 13–15 **d** 12–14

Homework 5C

1 a 10 cm², 14 cm **b** 16 cm², 16 cm **c** 16 m², 20 m **d** 36 mm², 30 mm **e** 200 m², 60 m
2 a 12 cm, 8 cm² **b** 22 cm, 28 cm² **c** 5 cm, 30 cm² **d** 5 cm, 16 cm **e** 10 cm, 5 cm or 5 cm, 10 cm
3 a 100 **b** 10 000

Homework 5D

1 33 cm² **2** 40 cm² **3** 60 cm² **4** 60 cm² **5** 500 cm²

Homework 5E

1 a 12 cm, 6 cm^2 **b** 24 cm, 24 cm^2 **c** 70 cm, 210 cm^2 **2 a** 40 cm^2 **b** 168 m^2 **c** 32 m^2 **3** 162 cm^2 **4 c** 24 cm^2

Homework 5F

1 a 20 cm^2 **b** 35 cm^2 **c** 308 cm^2 **d** 7.5 cm^2 **e** 54 cm^2 **f** 100 cm^2
2 a 24 cm^2 **b** 35 cm^2 **c** 12.5 cm^2 **d** 6 cm **e** 5 cm
3 a 1800 cm^2 **b** 144 cm^2 **c** 116 cm^2 **4** Two different triangles with an area of 40 cm^2

Homework 5G

1 a 15 cm^2 **b** 40 cm^2 **c** 16 m^2 **d** 240 cm^2 **2** 256 cm^2

Chapter 6

Homework 6A

1 a experiment **b** observation **c** sampling **d** observation **e** experiment **f** sampling
2 a **b** 0 twice, 1 once, 2 three times

Number	0	1	2
Frequency	11	5	20

3 a

Temperature (°C)	11–15	16–20	21–25	26–30	31–35	36–40	41–45
Frequency	2	6	4	5	4	2	1

b 16 **c** Kay found the difference using the frequency table, Derek found the difference using the actual temperatures
4 a 28 **b**

Age	11–20	21–30	31–40	41–50	51–60	61–70
Frequency	1	8	8	5	4	2

c 1, young people tend not to go to evening classes
5 a

Height (cm)	125–129	130–134	135–139	140–144	145–149	150–154
Frequency	2	2	6	9	4	5

b 140–144 cm **c** 18

Homework 6B

1 a 4 **b** 16, 10, 16 **c** Fri 3¾ symbols, Sat 5½ symbols
2 a 9h, 4½h, 9h, 6h, 10½h **b** difficult to show ⅚ of a symbol
3 a 20, 20, 15, 25, 15 **b** difficult to show single call-outs **c** new pictogram to show frequencies: 20, 20, 15, 25, 15, 16
4 pictogram to show frequencies: 30, 19, 12, 5, 1

Homework 6C

1 a Emmerdale **b** 50 **c** friends all of a similar age, friends will have similar interests, likely to be more girls
2 a 5 **b** 31 **c** 8 **d** No, each bar represents girls and boys
3

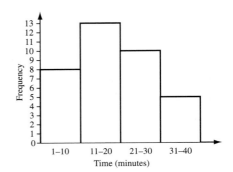

4 a

Time (min)	1–10	11–20	21–30	31–40
Frequency	8	13	10	5

b

5 Label axes Frequency and Brand of crisps preferred, scale frequency axis correctly and start from 0, make bars of equal width

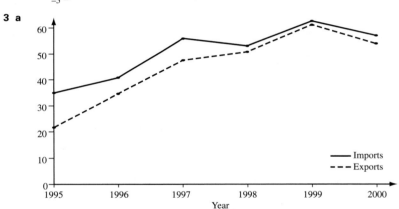

Homework 6D

1 a August, 250 pesetas   **b** 25 pesetas   **c** July   **d** 51 200 pesetas
2 a   **b** 15 °C

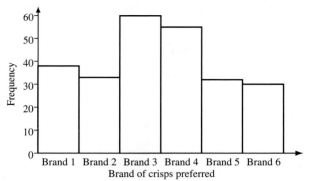

3 a   **b** smallest £1m (1999),
                                                                            greatest £13m (1995)

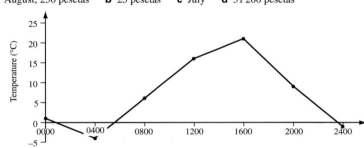

Chapter 7

Homework 7A

1 a $x + 4$ **b** $x - 7$ **c** $3 + k$ **d** $8 - t$ **e** $x + y$ **f** $4x$ **g** $5t$ **h** ab **i** $\frac{m}{2}$ **j** $\frac{p}{q}$

2 a $x + 4$ **b** $x - 5$ **3 a** $3n$ **b** $n + 2$ **c** $2n + 5$ **4 a** Frank $p + 2$, Chloe $p - 3$, Lizzie $2p$

5 a £4   **b** $£(10 - a)$ **c** $£(b - c)$ **6 a** 21   **b** $7z$ **7 a** £10   **b** $£\frac{r}{4}$ **c** $£\frac{p}{q}$

Homework 7B

1 a $3a$ **b** $5b$ **c** $9c$ **d** $4d$ **e** $3e$ **f** $8f$ **g** 0 **h** $-2h$ **i** $5i^2$ **j** $4j^2$
2 a $8x + 3y$ **b** $2m + 10p$ **c** $6x + 4$ **d** $5 + 3x$ **e** $8p$ **f** $6x - 2$ **g** $2p - 6$ **h** $6x - 2y$ **i** $7 + 6p - 3t$ **j** $6w - 4k$
3 a $2a + 8$ **b** $3b - 9$ **c** $5c + 5$ **d** $4e + 10$ **e** $12e - 4$ **f** $25m + 35$ **g** $10a + 4b$ **h** $6x - 8y$ **i** $12p + 3q$
   j $a^2 + 3a$ **k** $b^2 - 2b$ **l** $2x^2 + 2x$
4 a $3(a + 3)$ **b** $5(b + 5)$ **c** $2(3c + 2)$ **d** $2(4d - 3)$ **e** $5(2e - 3)$ **f** $5(f - 1)$ **g** $4(2g - 3)$ **h** $5(1 + 2h)$ **i** $7(3 - 2i)$
   j $x(x + 5)$ **k** $y(y + 4)$ **l** $z(z - 1)$

Homework 7C

1 a 7 **b** 13 **c** 23 **2 a** 2 **b** 14 **c** 32 **3 a** 8 **b** 24 **c** $4\frac{1}{2}$ **4 a** 4 **b** 0 **c** −2
5 a 35 **b** 60 **c** 85 **6 a** 10 **b** 28 **c** 1 **7 a** 2 **b** 3 **c** 5 **8 a** 1 **b** 4 **c** $5\frac{1}{2}$ **9 a** 10 **b** 2 **c** 1
10 a 21 **b** 33 **c** 45

Homework 7D

1 a 5 **b** 11 **c** 29 **2 a** 2 **b** 8 **c** 0 **3 a** 21 **b** 34 **c** −4 **4 a** 13 **b** 25 **c** 125
5 a 9 **b** 10 **c** 60 **6 a** 6 **b** 200 **c** 510 **7 a** 52 **b** 1040 **8 a** 7 **b** 60

Chapter 8

Homework 8A

1 312 **2** 561 **3** 2268 **4** 2047 **5** 3074 **6** 2464 **7** 3760 **8** 9219 **9** 20 020 **10** 38 646

Homework 8B

1 24 **2** 32 **3** 41 **4** 36 **5** 31 **6** 19 **7** 23 **8** 17 **9** 23 rem 5 **10** 17 rem 49

Homework 8C

1 384 **2** 40 **3 a** £3584 **b** $30 \times 100 = 3000$ **4** 27 **5** £728 **6** £2264 **7** £14 **8** 1536 **9** 23
10 a £1000 **b** £912

Homework 8D

1 a 3.7 **b** 8.7 **c** 5.3 **d** 18.8 **e** 0.4 **f** 26.3 **g** 3.8 **h** 10.1 **i** 11.1 **j** 12.0
2 a 6.72 **b** 4.46 **c** 1.97 **d** 3.49 **e** 5.81 **f** 2.56 **g** 21.80 **h** 12.99 **i** 2.30 **j** 5.56
3 a 4.6 **b** 0.09 **c** 5.716 **d** 4.56 **e** 2.10 **f** 0.763 **g** 7.1 **h** 8.90 **i** 23.781 **j** 1.0
4 a 7 **b** 9 **c** 3 **d** 8 **e** 8 **f** 3 **g** 2 **h** 2 **i** 5 **j** 4

Homework 8E

1 a 9.9 **b** 21.3 **c** 40.3 **d** 13.32 **e** 7.76 **f** 12.59 **g** 30.8 **h** 21.2 **i** 22.25 **j** 7.78 **k** 13.06 **l** 27.96
2 a 2.4 **b** 4.5 **c** 1.9 **d** 5 **e** 4.11 **f** 5.93 **g** 3.32 **h** 1.77 **i** 2.7 **j** 0.6 **k** 8.8 **l** 2.48

Homework 8F

1 a 6.9 **b** 9.6 **c** 18.4 **d** 76.5 **e** 211.2 **2 a** 4.28 **b** 10.35 **c** 32.82 **d** 35.52 **e** 2.25
3 a 2.4 **b** 1.9 **c** 2.4 **d** 1.47 **e** 0.13 **4 a** 2.25 **b** 1.44 **c** 0.85 **d** 2.62 **e** 0.7875 **5** packs of 6 **6** £91.75

Homework 8G

1 a 43.68 **b** 78.6 **c** 29.92 **d** 188.25 **e** 867.2 **2 a** £18.72 **b** £5.04 **c** £31.50
3 a 256.25 F **b** $44.48 **c** 137.70 DM

Homework 8H

1 a 0.46 **b** 1.56 **c** 1.84 **d** 0.06 **e** 0.28 **f** 0.25 **g** 7.56 **h** 5.04 **i** 1.68 **j** 3.9
2 a i 8 **ii** 8.88, 0.88 **b i** 15 **ii** 14.88, 0.12 **c i** 20 **ii** 21.42, 1.42 **d i** 21 **ii** 16.25, 4.75

Homework 8 I

1 a $\frac{3}{10}$ **b** $\frac{4}{5}$ **c** $\frac{9}{10}$ **d** $\frac{7}{100}$ **e** $\frac{2}{25}$ **f** $\frac{3}{20}$ **g** $\frac{3}{4}$ **h** $\frac{12}{25}$ **i** $\frac{8}{25}$ **j** $\frac{27}{100}$
2 a 0.25 **b** 0.4 **c** 0.7 **d** 0.45 **e** 0.875
3 a 0.2, 0.3, $\frac{2}{5}$ **b** 0.6, $\frac{7}{10}$, 0.8 **c** 0.2, $\frac{1}{4}$, 0.4 **d** 0.29, $\frac{3}{10}$, 0.32 **e** 0.78, $\frac{4}{5}$, 0.81

Chapter 9

Homework 9A

1 a 1:3 **b** 1:5 **c** 1:6 **d** 1:3 **e** 2:3 **f** 3:5 **g** 5:8 **h** 15:2 **i** 2:5 **j** 5:2
2 a 1:4 **b** 3:4 **c** 1:8 **d** 2:5 **e** 2:5 **f** 8:15 **g** 10:3 **h** 1:3 **i** 3:8 **j** 1:5
3 a $\frac{1}{4}$ **b** $\frac{3}{4}$ **4 a** $\frac{2}{5}$ **b** $\frac{3}{5}$ **5 a** $\frac{1}{10}$ **b** $\frac{9}{10}$

Homework 9B

1 a £2:£8 **b** £4:£8 **c** £10:£30 **d** 10 g:50 g **e** 1 h:9 h **f** 10 kg:15 kg **g** 18 days:12 days **h** 30 m:40 m
i £1.50:£3.50 **j** 15 h:9 h
2 a 300 **b** 100 **3** 2 m and 18 m **4** 400 **5** 45 **6** £6 **7** £30 and £36
8 a 1:1.5 **b** 1:2.5 **c** 1:1.25 **d** 1:1.6 **e** 1:2.1

Homework 9C

1 20   **2** 80   **3 a** 15*l*   **b** 25*l*   **4 a** 80 kg   **b** 5 kg   **5** 90   **6 a** 200 g   **b** 320 g   **7 a** £4000   **b** £6000

Homework 9D

1 15 mph   **2** 180 miles   **3** 46 mph   **4** 2pm
5 a 30 mph   **b** 50 km/h   **c** 20 miles   **d** 50 km   **e** 3 hours 15 minutes   **f** 3 hours 36 minutes
6 a 130 km   **b** 52 km/h   **7 a** 30 minutes   **b** 12 mph   **8 a** 1.25 h   **b** 45 miles

Homework 9E

1 £8   **2** £2.16   **3** £49.60   **4 a** 675 pesetas   **b** 26   **5 a** £27.20   **b** 11   **6 a** 6*l*   **b** 405 miles   **7** 48*s*
8 a i 50 g, 2, 40 g, 100 g   **ii** 200 g, 8, 160 g, 400 g   **iii** 250 g, 10, 200 g, 500 g   **b** 60

Homework 9F

1 a large size, 4.0 g/p   **b** 200 g bar, 2.2 g/p   **c** 500 g tin, 0.64 g/p   **d** large jar, 3.8 g/p
2 large size   **3** 72p, 66p, 70p, 65p. 3*l* bottle   **4** 3 for the price of 2, 1500 g for £3.38

Chapter 10

Homework 10A

1 a   **b**    **c**    **d**   **e**

2 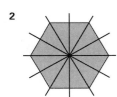   **3 a** 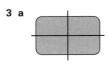   **b**   **c**   **d**   **e**

4 a 1   **b** 1   **c** 2   **5 a** 1   **b** 1   **c** 2   **d** 1   **e** 1
6 a e.g. 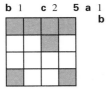   **b** e.g. 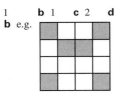   **c** e.g.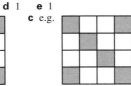

Homework 10B

1 a 4   **b** 2   **c** 2   **d** 3   **e** 2   **2 a** 5   **b** 6   **c** 2   **d** 2   **e** 8   **3 a** 2   **b** 2   **c** 4   **d** 4   **e** 5
4 a 1   **b** 2   **c** 2   **d** 1   **e** 2   **f** 1   **g** 2   **h** 2   **5 a** 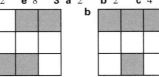   **b**

Homework 10C

1 a 9   **b** 5   **c** 2   **d** 2
2 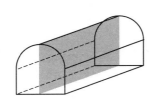   **3 a** 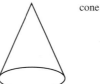 cone

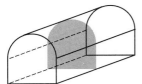

4 a 2   **b** 0   **c** 2   **d** 2 (ignoring the cable)

Chapter 11

▰ Homework 11A

1 a 2 **b** 15 **c** 101 **d** 1 **e** $6\frac{1}{2}$ **2 a** E **b** C4 **c** ← **d** ♣ **e** ∈ **3 a** 40 **b** 3 **c** 112
4 a 30 **b** 21–25 marks **c** the 5 students in the 26–30 interval might all have scored fewer rhan 30 marks
5 a

Time in minutes	0–3	4–7	8–11	12–15
Frequency	9	13	6	2

b 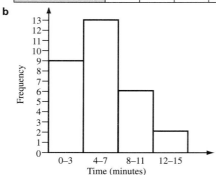 **c** 8 **d** 4–7 minutes **e** e.g. open more check-outs

▰ Homework 11B

1 a 15 **b** 34 **c** 0 **d** 11 **e** 1.6 **2 a** 71 kg **b** 62 kg **c** median, it is a central value
3 a 2 **b** 3 **c** No, all scores have about the same frequency **4 a** e.g. 7, 8, 9, **10**, 15, **20, 20** **b** e.g. 7, 8, 9, **10, 10**, 15, **20, 20**
5

```
2 | 7
3 | 5, 8
4 | 0, 3, 5, 8, 9
5 | 2, 5, 7, 9            (2 | 7 means 27)
6 | 2, 7, 8
7 | 2, 7, 8
8 | 0, 1, 7              The median is 57 marks
```

6 a 72 **b** 101 **c** pulse rate increases after exercise

▰ Homework 11C

1 a 4 **b** 24 **c** 333 **d** 3.3 **e** 2 **2 a** 22.1 **b** 98.9 **c** 9.8 **d** 181.6 **e** 0.8
3 3 hours 18 minutes **4 a** £800 **b** £910 **c i** 5 **ii** 2 **d** median – the 2 extreme amounts are not used
5 a 62 **b** 63 **c** Fay **d** 3 **6 a** 31 **b** 47

▰ Homework 11D

1 a 13 **b** 14 **c** 32 **d** 2.7 **e** 10 **2 a** 25 **b** 16 **c** 5 years **d**

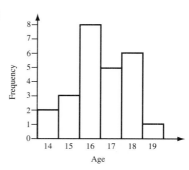

3 a 76 °C **b** 15 °C **c** Similar means, but Crete's temperatures are more consistent
4 a 10KG – 26, 10RH – 25, 10PB – 27 **b** 10KG – 2, 10RH – 8, 10PB – 5
c i 10PB – highest mean **ii** 10KG – smallest range
5 a boys – 37, girls – 37 **b** boys – 28, girls – 36 **c** same median, but boys more consistent

▰ Homework 11E

1 a i mode 6, median 4, mean 4 **ii** mode 15, median 15, mean 15.1 **iii** mode 32, median 32, mean 33
b i mean, balanced data **ii** mode, appears 6 times **iii** median, 46 is an extreme value
2 a mode 135 g, median 141 g, mean 143g **b** mean, takes all weights into account
3 a 71 kg **b** 70 kg **c** median, 53 kg is an extreme weight **4 a** 59 **b** 54 **c** median, the higher average

▰ Homework 11F

1 1.6 **2 a** 5 **b** 1 **c** 3.45 **3 a** 2 **b** 2 **c** 1.7 **4 a** 14 **b** 7.6

Chapter 12

Homework 12A

1 a $\frac{1}{10}$ **b** $\frac{2}{5}$ **c** $\frac{1}{4}$ **d** $\frac{3}{20}$ **e** $\frac{3}{4}$ **f** $\frac{7}{20}$ **g** $\frac{3}{25}$ **h** $\frac{7}{25}$ **i** $\frac{14}{25}$ **j** $\frac{9}{50}$ **k** $\frac{21}{50}$ **l** $\frac{3}{50}$
2 a 0.87 **b** 0.25 **c** 0.33 **d** 0.05 **e** 0.01 **f** 0.72 **g** 0.58 **h** 0.175 **i** 0.085 **j** 0.682 **k** 1.5 **l** 1.32
3

Percentage	Fraction	Decimal
10%	$\frac{1}{10}$	0.1
20%	$\frac{2}{10} = \frac{1}{5}$	0.2
30%	$\frac{3}{10}$	0.3
40%	$\frac{4}{10} = \frac{2}{5}$	0.4
50%	$\frac{5}{10} = \frac{1}{2}$	0.5
60%	$\frac{6}{10} = \frac{3}{5}$	0.6
70%	$\frac{7}{10}$	0.7
80%	$\frac{8}{10} = \frac{4}{5}$	0.8
90%	$\frac{9}{10}$	0.9

4 55% **5** 16% **6** 23% **7** 69% **8 a** $\approx 20\%$ **b** $\approx 75\%$ **c** $\approx 90\%$

Homework 12B

1 a £50 **b** £12 **c** 212 kg **d** 63 cm **e** £18.48 **f** 177.5 g **g** £0.72 **h** 304 m **i** £2.52 **j** £9.80 **k** 13.6 *l* **l** £297.60
2 208 **3** Y7 240, Y8 230, Y9 210, Y10 220, Y11 200 **4** 378*t*, 63*t*, 9*t* **5 a** £7 **b** £14.35 **c** £42 **6** £600

Homework 12C

1 a £84 **b** £165 **c** 920 m **d** 400 kg **e** £54.60 **f** £39.60 **g** 141.6 cm **h** £46.72 **i** 1017.5 g **j** £123.84
2 £33 800 **3** £54.18, £42.14, £109.32, £5.47, £114.79 **4 a** £2160 **b** £2320 **c** £2480
5 clock: £21.15, wallet: £17.86, towel: £15.04, bookmark: £7.52

Homework 12D

1 a £18 **b** £120 **c** 63 kg **d** 440 m **e** £247 **f** 60 cm **g** 232 g **h** £327.25 **i** 12 kg **j** £39.69
2 £6384 **3** 2112 **4** £459 **5 a** £24 **b** £104 **c** £33.60

Homework 12E

1 a 20% **b** 75% **c** 70% **d** 25% **e** 30% **f** 17% **g** 45% **h** 65% **i** 46% **j** 44%
2 a 33.3% **b** 66.7% **c** 16.7% **d** 83.3% **e** 41.7%
3 a 90% **b** 30% **c** 58% **d** 79% **e** 98% **f** 24% **g** 8% **h** 1% **i** 12.5% **j** 130%
4 a $\frac{48}{60} = \frac{4}{5}$ **b** 0.8 **c** 80% **5 a** 20%, $\frac{1}{4}$, 0.3 **b** 3%, 0.05, $\frac{1}{10}$ **c** $\frac{3}{4}$, 80%, 0.85 **6 a** 70% **b** 30%
7 81%, 62%, 55%, 77%, 55%

Homework 12F

1 a 20% **b** 25% **c** 10% **d** 75% **e** 80% **f** 46% **g** 33.3% **h** 30% **i** 67.5% **j** 23.8%
2 a 75% **b** 37.5% **3 a** 60% **b** 40% **4** 29.3% **5 a** 66.7% **b** 50% **c** 50.0% **d** 66.6%

Chapter 13

Homework 13A

1 4 **2** 2 **3** 5 **4** 6 **5** 2 **6** 4 **7** 3 **8** 1 **9** 5 **10** 6 **11** 10 **12** 18 **13** 12 **14** 9 **15** 20

Homework 13B

1 1 **2** 7 **3** −2 **4** 4 **5** 5 **6** 8 **7** 3 **8** 1 **9** 3.5 **10** 14 **11** 9 **12** 10

Homework 13C

1 3 **2** 4 **3** 4 **4** 5 **5** 10 **6** 6 **7** 6 **8** 3 **9** 16 **10** 6 **11** 5 **12** 2

Homework 13D

1 3 **2** 7 **3** 1 **4** 5 **5** 6 **6** 3 **7** 2 **8** −2 **9** −3 **10** 1.5 **11** 1.25 **12** 1.1

Homework 13E

1 2   **2** 4   **3** 7   **4** 3   **5** 4   **6** 5   **7** 2   **8** –2   **9** 0   **10** 2.5   **11** 9   **12** –3

Homework 13F

1 7 years old   **2** 8 years old   **3** 5   **4** 6 cm, 6 cm, 5 cm, 10 cm, 5 cm   **5** crime: 20, science fiction: 28, romance: 17   **6** 5
7 12   **8 a** 50p: 10, £1: 20, £2: 14   **b** £53

Chapter 14

Homework 14A

1 a i £60   **ii** £80   **iii** £120   **b i** 50   **ii** 40   **iii** 25   **2 a i** £300   **ii** £200   **iii** £175   **b i** 400   **ii** 200   **iii** 150
3 a line graph passing through (250, 33), (500, 51) and (750, 69)   **b** about £45

Homework 14B

1 a i 10.30   **ii** 11.10   **iii** 12.00   **b i** 50 km/h   **ii** 75 km/h   **iii** 50 km/h
2 a 20 km   **b** 40 km   **c** 60 km/h   **d** 100 km/h
3

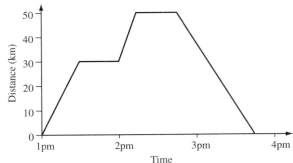

Homework 14C

1

x	0	1	2	3	4
y	1	2	3	4	5

2

x	0	1	2	3	4
y	1	3	5	7	9

3

x	0	1	2	3	4
y	1	4	7	10	13

4

x	0	1	2	3	4
y	–1	0	1	2	3

5 a graphs of $y = x - 2$ and $y = 2x - 1$ **b** (–1, –3)   **6 a** graphs of $y = 2x$ and $y = x + 2$ **b** (2, 4)

Homework 14D

1 end points at (0, 3) and (5, 13)   **2** end points at (0, –1) and (5, 14)   **3** end points at (0, –2) and (12, 4)
4 end points at (–2, –3) and (2, 5)   **5** end points at (–6, 2) and (6, 8)
6 a end points at (0, –1) and (5, 14), (0, 3) and (5, 13)   **b** (4, 11)
7 a end points at (0, –3) and (6, 21), (0, 2) and (6, 20)   **b** (5, 17)
8 a end points at (0, 1) and (12, 7), (0, 2) and (12, 6)   **b** (6, 4)
9 a end points at (0, 3) and (4, 11), (0, –1) and (4, 7)   **b** no, the lines are parallel
10 a

x	0	1	2	3	4	5	6
y	6	5	4	3	2	1	0

b graph of $x + y = 3$

Chapter 15

Homework 15A

1 a 25°   **b** 35°   **c** 55°   **d** 84°   **e** 85°   **f** 145°   **g** 168°   **h** 200°
2 angles drawn: **a** 30°   **b** 42°   **c** 55°   **d** 68°   **e** 75°   **f** 140°   **g** 164°   **h** 245°
3 three acute angles drawn: estimated and measured with differences

▰ Homework 15B

1 $60°$ **2** $45°$ **3** $300°$ **4** $120°$ **5** $27°$ **6** $101°$ **7** $100°$ **8** $60°$ **9** $59°$ **10** $50°$ **11** $100°$ **12** $138°$

▰ Homework 15C

1 a $120°$ **b** $45°$ **c** $50°$ **2 a** $60°$ **b** $75°$ **c** $40°$ **3 a** $x = 60°, y = 120°$ **b** $x = 30°, y = 140°$ **c** $x = 44°, y = 58°$

▰ Homework 15D

1 a $70°$ **b** $40°$ **c** $88°$ **d** $12°$ **e** $42°$ **f** $118°$
2 a yes, total is $180°$ **b** no, total is $190°$ **c** no, total is $160°$ **d** yes, total is $180°$ **e** yes, total is $180°$ **f** no, total is $190°$
3 a $70°$ **b** $60°$ **c** $10°$ **d** $43°$ **e** $5°$ **f** $41°$ **4 a** $60°$ **b** equilateral triangle **c** all sides equal in length
5 a $55°$ **b** isosceles triangle **c** equal in length **6** $x = 30°, y = 60°$ **7 a** $119°$ **b** $70°$

▰ Homework 15E

1 a $70°$ **b** $120°$ **c** $65°$ **d** $70°$ **e** $70°$ **f** $126°$
2 a no, total is $350°$ **b** yes, total is $360°$ **c** yes, total is $360°$ **d** no, total is $370°$ **e** no, total is $350°$ **f** yes, total is $360°$
3 a $90°$ **b** $80°$ **c** $80°$ **d** $46°$ **e** $30°$ **f** $137°$ **4 a** $290°$ **b** reflex **c** kite or arrowhead

▰ Homework 15F

1 a $x = 60°, y = 120°$ **b** $x = 90°, y = 90°$ **c** $x = 108°, y = 72°$ **d** $x = 120°, y = 60°$ **e** $x = 135°, y = 45°$
2 a pentagon divided into 3 triangles, $3 \times 180° = 540°$ **b** $80°$ **3** 360 is not divisible by 25

▰ Homework 15G

1 a $a = 60°$ **b** $b = 50°$ **c** $c = 152°$ **d** $d = e = 62°$ **e** $f = g = 115°$ **f** $h = i = 72°$
2 a $a = b = c = 55°$ **b** $d = 132°, e = 48°$ **c** $f = 78°, g = 102°$ **3 a** $70°$ **b** $68°$

▰ Homework 15H

1 a $a = 110°, b = 100°$ **b** $c = 68°, d = 108°$ **c** $e = 90°, f = 105°$
2 a $a = c = 130°, b = 50°$ **b** $d = f = 45°, e = 135°$ **c** $g = i = 139°, h = 41°$
3 a $a = 120°, b = 50°$ **b** $c = d = 90°$ **c** $e = 96°, f = 56°$
4 a $a = c = 125°, b = 55°$ **b** $d = f = 70°, e = 110°$ **c** $g = i = 117°, h = 63°$

▰ Homework 15I

1 a $062°$ **b** $130°$ **c** $220°$ **d** $285°$ **2 a** $160°$ **b** $095°$ **c** $005°$ **d** $275°$

Chapter 16

▰ Homework 16A (Answers may vary, depending on the value of π used)

1 a 9.4 cm **b** 28.3 cm **c** 31.4 cm **d** 37.7 cm **e** 66.0 cm
2 a 12.6 cm **b** 22.0 cm **c** 44.0 cm **d** 62.8 cm **e** 78.6 cm
3 48 m **4 a** 314.2 m **b** 16 **5** 51.4 m **6** 12.7 cm

▰ Homework 16B (Answers may vary, depending on the value of π used)

1 a 12.6 cm² **b** 113.1 cm² **c** 201.1 cm² **d** 314.2 cm² **e** 452.5 cm²
2 a 3.1 cm² **b** 28.3 cm² **c** 78.6 cm² **d** 227.0 cm² **e** 490.9 cm² **3 a** 2.5 m **b** 0.5 m²
4 a 113.1 m² **b** 7 m **c** 154.0 m² **d** 40.9 m² **5 a** 357 m **b** 6963 m² **6 a** 15.9 cm **b** 8.0 cm **c** 199.0 cm²

▰ Homework 16C

1 24 cm³ **2** 30 cm³ **3** 35 cm³ **4** 40 cm³

▰ Homework 16D

1 a i 72 cm³ **ii** 108 cm² **b i** 100 cm³ **ii** 160 cm² **c i** 180 cm³ **ii** 222 cm² **d i** 125 cm³ **ii** 150 cm²
2 24 cm³, 5 cm, 5 cm, 6 cm **3** 90 m³ **4 a** 60 cm³ **b** 160 cm³ **c** 120 cm³ **5** 24 **6 a** 544 cm³ **b** 225 m³

Chapter 17

▰ Homework 17A

1 a 1 cm, 2 cm **b** 2.5 cm, 5.0 cm **c** 3.0 cm, 6.0 cm **4** 5 cm **5** 2.9 cm

███ **Homework 17B**

3 You can draw this triangle by drawing sides at 60° to each other; measure 5 cm along one side; use compasses from this point to find 6 cm intersection with other line. **4 b** rhombus

███ **Homework 17C**

1 a yes **b** no **c** yes **d** no **e** yes **f** no **2 a** 2 **b** 3 **c** 1 **d** 3

Chapter 18

███ **Homework 18A**

1 a likely **b** impossible **c** very likely **d** very unlikely **e** certain **f** evens **g** unlikely
2 e

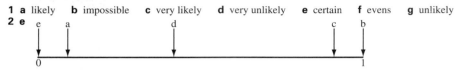

███ **Homework 18B**

1 a $\frac{1}{13}$ **b** $\frac{3}{13}$ **c** $\frac{1}{4}$ **d** $\frac{2}{13}$ **e** $\frac{1}{52}$ **f** $\frac{1}{26}$ **g** $\frac{1}{2}$ **2 a** $\frac{1}{10}$ **b** $\frac{1}{2}$ **c** $\frac{3}{5}$ **d** $\frac{2}{5}$ **e** $\frac{3}{10}$ **3 a** $\frac{2}{9}$ **b** $\frac{1}{3}$ **c** $\frac{5}{9}$ **d** 0
4 a $\frac{1}{5}$ **b** $\frac{1}{5}$ **c** $\frac{3}{5}$ **d** $\frac{4}{5}$ **e** $\frac{4}{5}$ **5 a i** $\frac{1}{5}$ **ii** $\frac{1}{3}$ **iii** $\frac{7}{15}$ **b** they add up to 1 **c** all possible outcomes are used **6** 20%

███ **Homework 18C**

1 a $\frac{19}{20}$ **b** 35% **c** 0.2 **d** $\frac{35}{36}$ **2 a i** $\frac{1}{13}$ **ii** $\frac{12}{13}$ **b i** $\frac{1}{4}$ **ii** $\frac{3}{4}$ **c i** $\frac{2}{13}$ **ii** $\frac{11}{13}$ **3 a i** $\frac{5}{11}$ **ii** $\frac{6}{11}$ **b i** $\frac{1}{2}$ **ii** $\frac{1}{2}$

███ **Homework 18D**

1 a $\frac{1}{5}, \frac{3}{20}, \frac{1}{5}, \frac{9}{50}, \frac{17}{100}, \frac{7}{40}, \frac{17}{100}$ **b** $\frac{1}{6}$ **2 a** $\frac{11}{60}, \frac{17}{120}, \frac{7}{40}, \frac{3}{20}, \frac{13}{60}, \frac{2}{15}$ **b** 20 **c** yes, all frequencies are close to 20
3 a i 90 **ii** 60 **iii** 30 **b** 0.4

███ **Homework 18E**

1 a 7 **b** 2 and 12 **c** $\frac{1}{36}$ **d i** $\frac{1}{18}$ **ii** $\frac{1}{12}$ **iii** $\frac{1}{6}$ **iv** $\frac{1}{2}$ **v** $\frac{1}{6}$ **vi** $\frac{1}{4}$ **2 a** $\frac{1}{12}$ **b** $\frac{1}{4}$ **c** $\frac{1}{6}$
3 a (H, 1), (H, 2), (H, 3), (H, 4), (H, 5), (T, 1), (T, 2), (T, 3), (T, 4), (T, 5) **b** $\frac{3}{10}$ **4 b i** $\frac{1}{5}$ **ii** $\frac{1}{25}$ **iii** 0 **iv** $\frac{4}{25}$ **v** $\frac{9}{25}$

Chapter 19

███ **Homework 19A**

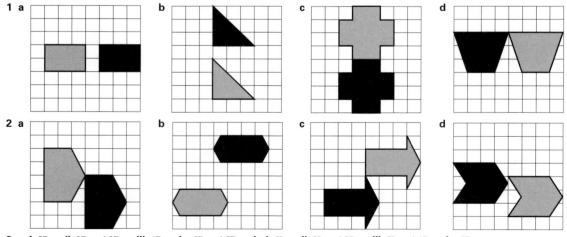

3 a i 5R **ii** 3R and 2D **iii** 4D **iv** 5R and 5D **b i** 5L **ii** 2L and 2D **iii** 5L and 4D **iv** 5D
  c i 3L and 2U **ii** 2R and 2U **iii** 3L and 2D **iv** 2R and 3D **d i** 5R and 1D **ii** 5U **iii** 3R and 2U **iv** 5L and 1U
4 A'(6, 5), B'(9, 5), C'(9, 7), D'(6, 7)

Homework 19B

1 a 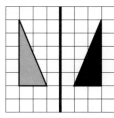   **b** 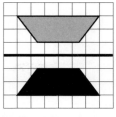   **c** 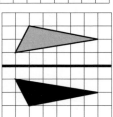   **d**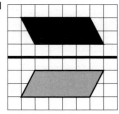

2 a 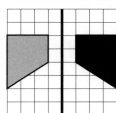   **b** 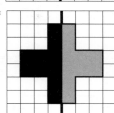   **c** 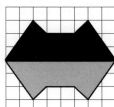   **d**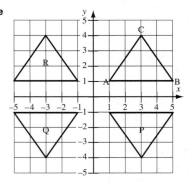

3 a and b

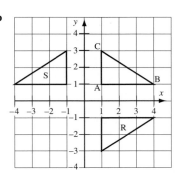

4 a, b, c, d and e

3 c congruent

4 f a reflection in the *y*-axis

Homework 19C

1 a 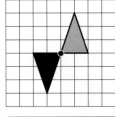   **b** 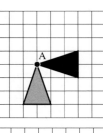   **c** 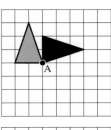   **d**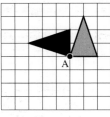

2 a 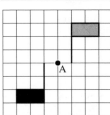   **b** 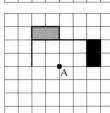   **c** 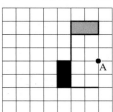   **d**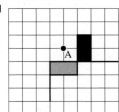

3 a, b and c

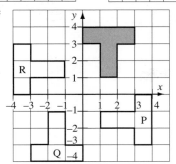

d a rotation of 90° clockwise about O

4 a A(1, 1), B(3, 1), C(3, 3), D(1, 3) **b, c, d**

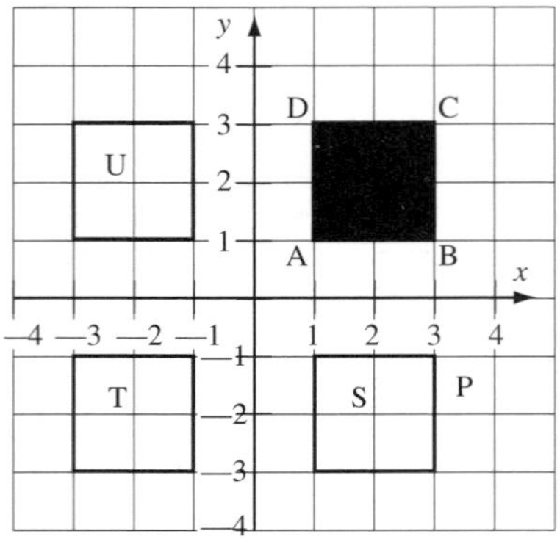

e corresponding vertices have same pairs of coordinates switching round and changing signs

Homework 19D

1 a

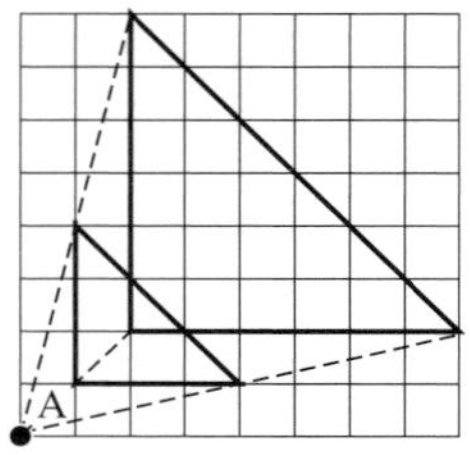

b

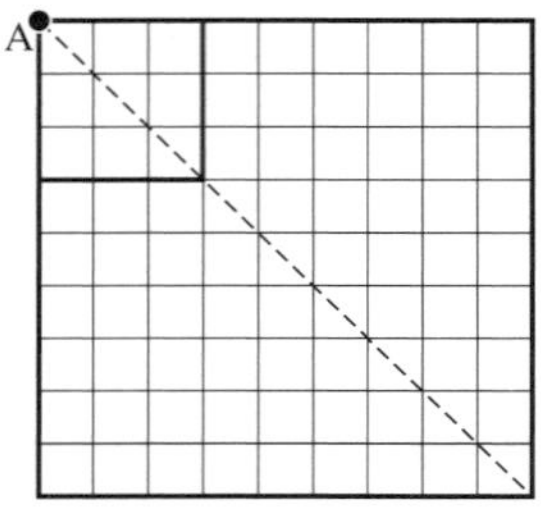

2 a

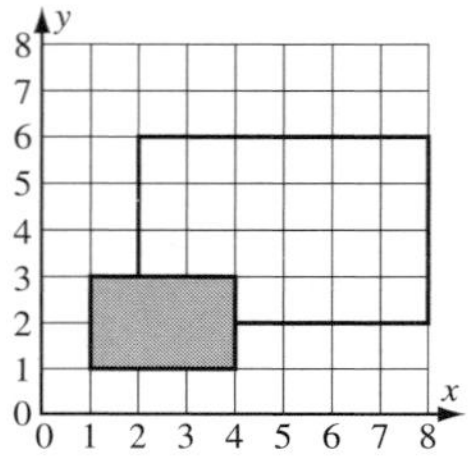

b

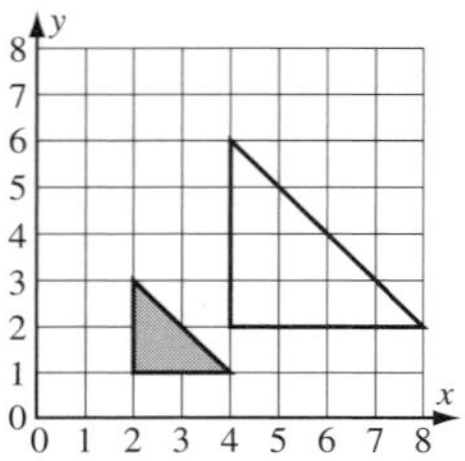

c

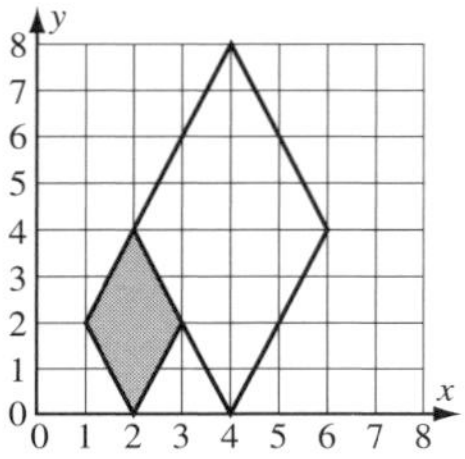

d

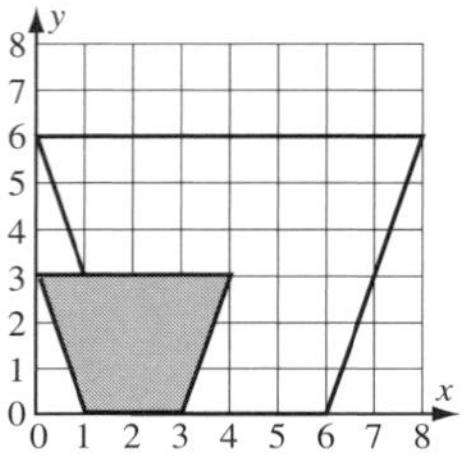

Homework 19E

1 a

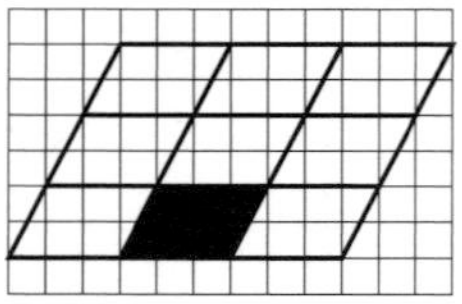

b

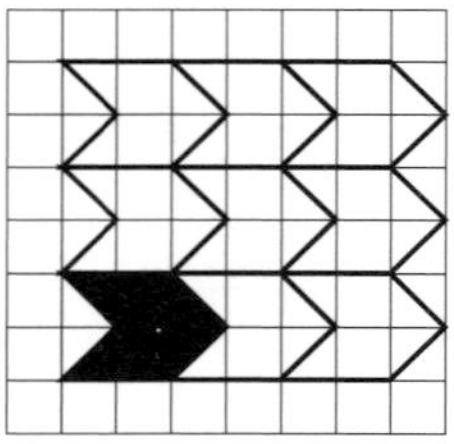

c

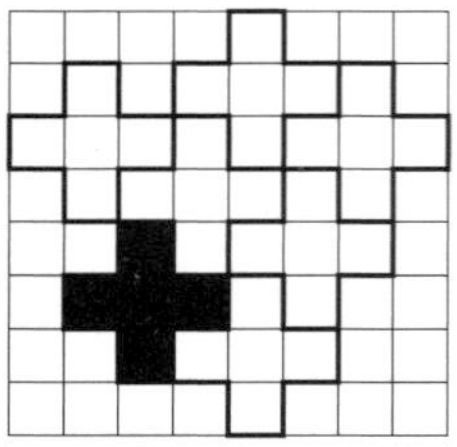

d

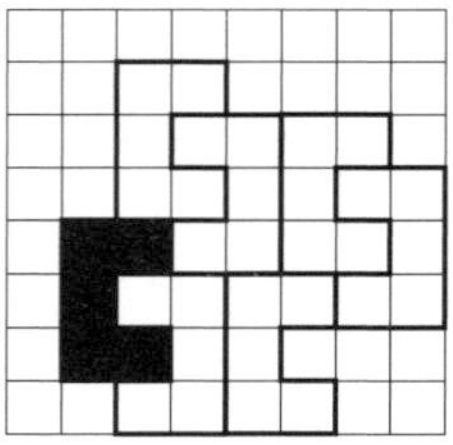

2

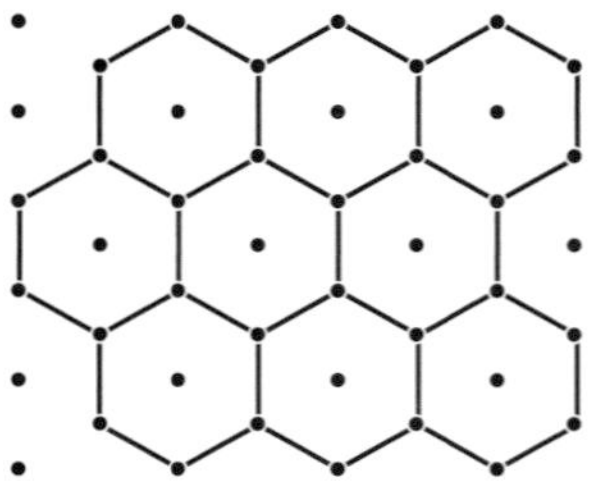

Chapter 20

Homework 20A

1 a i 90 cm by 60 cm **ii** 90 cm by 60 cm **iii** 60 cm by 60 cm **iv** 90 cm by 45 cm **b** 10 800 cm^2 **2 b** 4.12 m
3 a 10.5 km **b** 12.5 km **c** 20 km **d** 13 km **e** 4 km **4 a** 4.5 km **b** 10 km **c** 7.5 km **d** 16 km **e** 9.5 km

Homework 20B

1 b and **d**   **4 a i** 5   **ii** 8   **iii** 5

Homework 20C

3 a i 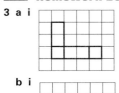   **ii** 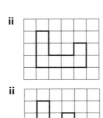   **iii**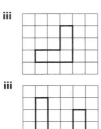

b i   **ii**   **iii**

Chapter 21

Homework 21A

1 centimetres   **2** kilometres (or metres)   **3** millimetres   **4** kilograms   **5** litres   **6** grams   **7** metres   **8** grams

Homework 21B

1 1.55 m   **2** 9.5 cm   **3** 0.78 m   **4** 3.1 km   **5** 3.1 m   **6** 3.05 m   **7** 15.6 cm   **8** 2.18 km   **9** 1.07 m   **10** 13.24 m
11 0.175 km   **12** 0.083 m   **13** 62 cm   **14** 21.3   **15** 5.12   **16** 8.15   **17** 2.3t **18** 3.2 cl **19** 1.36 l **20** 5.8 l
21 0.95t **22** 0.12 kg   **23** 0.15 l **24** 3.5 l **25** 54 cl **26** 2.06t **27** 7.5 l **28** 3.8 kg   **29** 6.05 l **30** 0.015 l
31 6.3 m³   **32** 45 cm³   **33** 2.35 m³   **34** 0.72 m³   **35** 820 cm   **36** 71 000 m   **37** 8600 mm   **38** 156 mm   **39** 83 cm
40 5150 m   **41** 18.5   **42** 275 cm

Homework 21C

1 60 inches   **2** 15 feet   **3** 5280 yards   **4** 96 ounces   **5** 70 pounds   **6** 4480 pounds   **7** 32 pints   **8** 84 inches
9 72 inches   **10** 33 feet   **11** 80 ounces   **12** 6 feet   **13** 84 pounds   **14** 13 yards   **15** 448 ounces   **16** 2.5 miles
17 96 pints   **18** 10 560 feet   **19** 7 feet   **20** 7.5 stones   **21** 6 gallons   **22** 3 pounds   **23** 7 yards   **24** 10 tonnes
25 126 720 inches   **26** 16 pounds   **27** 10 gallons   **28** 20 stones   **29** 6 miles   **30** 71 680 ounces

Homework 21D

1 a 13.2 lb   **b** 17.6 lb   **c** 33 lb   **d** 70.4 lb   **e** 99 lb   **2 a** 4.5 kg   **b** 8.2 kg   **c** 11.4 kg   **d** 18.2 kg   **e** 25.5 kg
3 80 kg   **4** 52 kg   **5** 50.9 kg   **6** Christine   **7** 12 lb bag   **8** 5 lb parcel

Homework 21E

1 a 3.5 pints   **b** 14 pints   **c** 43.75 pints   **d** 105 pints   **e** 131.25 pints   **2 a** 4 l **b** 11 l **c** 20 l **d** 24 l **e** 57 l
3 yes, it holds 17.5 pints   **4** 8$\frac{3}{4}$ pints   **5** 87$\frac{1}{2}$ pints   **6** container X   **7** 5 l can   **8** 3 l of milk

Homework 21F

1 a 32 km   **b** 48 km   **c** 80 km   **d** 104 km   **e** 192 km   **2 a** 10 miles   **b** 15 miles   **c** 25 miles   **d** 45 miles
e 187.5 miles   **3** 75 mph   **4** 42 km
5

Birmingham	192	160	336
	Leeds	120	144
		Liverpool	280
			Newcastle

6 Allan   **7** London to Lisbon   **8** Bill

Homework 21G

1 a 22.5 l **b** 54 l **c** 121.5 l **d** 225 l **e** 324 l **2 a** 4 g   **b** 10 g   **c** 16 g   **d** 60 g   **e** 200 g   **3** 711.1 gallons
4 40.5 l **5** 17 gallons   **6** 16 km/l **7** 4500 l **8** 90 days

Homework 21H

1 a 78 ins   **b** 195 ins   **c** 312 ins   **d** 390 ins   **e** 468 ins   **2 a** 90 cm   **b** 150 cm   **c** 210 cm   **d** 300 cm   **e** 900 cm
3 a 1.2 m   **b** 1.3 m   **c** 1.5 m   **d** 1.9 m   **e** 2.6 m   **4** 174 cm   **5** 20.31 m or 19.80 depending on conversion used
6 1625 m or 1584 m   **7** 3 ft 6 ins pool   **8** 7 m of cable

Chapter 22

■ Homework 22A

1

Time in minutes	10 or less	Between 10 and 30	30 or more
Angle on pie chart	48°	114°	198°

2

GCSE passes	9 or more	7 or 8	5 or 6	4 or less
Angle on pie chart	40°	200°	100°	20°

3 a

Main use	e-mail	Internet	Word-processing	Games
Angle on pie chart	50°	130°	30°	150°

b most used the computer for playing games and only a few used it for word-processing
c not enough in sample, only a small age range of people, probably only boys, etc.

4 a

Type of programme	Comedy	Drama	Films	Soaps	Sport
Angle on pie chart	54°	33°	63°	78°	132°

b no, only asked people who are likely to have similar interests, e.g. sport
5 a 25%   **b** rarely   **c** no, it only shows proportions   **d** What is your age? How often do you take exercise? How often do you see a doctor? etc.

■ Homework 22B

1 a and b

c ≈ 64.5 kg
d ≈ 123.5 cm

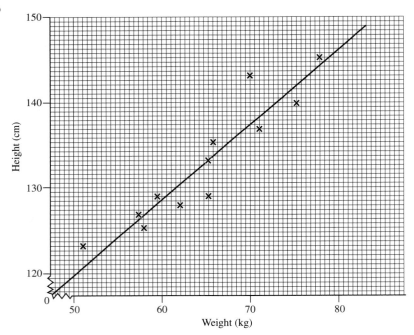

2 a and b

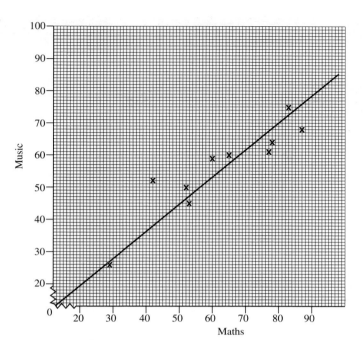

c Hazel
d ≈40 marks
e ≈ 87 marks

Chapter 23

▬ Homework 23A

1 $7 \times 11 \times 13 \times 6 = 6006$, $7 \times 11 \times 13 \times 7 = 7007$ **2** $3 \times 7 \times 13 \times 137 \times 6 = 60606$, $3 \times 7 \times 13 \times 137 \times 7 = 70707$
3 $7 \times 9 = 8^2 - 1 = 63$, $8 \times 10 = 9^2 - 1 = 80$ **4** $7 \times 11 = 9^2 - 4 = 77$, $8 \times 12 = 10^2 - 1 = 96$ **5** 9009   **6** 80808   **7** 9999
8 9996   **9** 15015   **10** 151515   **11** 999996   **12** 999999

▬ Homework 23B

1 a 12, 14, 16 : +2   **b** 15, 18, 21 : +3   **c** 32, 64, 128 : ×2   **d** 33, 40, 47 : +7   **e** 30 000, 300 000, 3 000 000 : ×10
f 25, 36, 49 : square numbers
2 a 34, 55 : add previous two terms   **b** 23, 30 : add one more each time
3 a 112, 224, 448 : ×2   **b** 38, 45, 52 : +7   **c** 63, 127, 255 : add twice the difference each time
d 30, 25, 19 : subtract one more each time   **e** 38, 51, 66 : add add two more each time   **f** 25, 32, 40 : add one more each time
g 13, 15, 16 : +2, +1   **h** 20, 23, 26 : +3   **i** 32, 40, 49 : add one more each time   **j** 0, −5, −11 : subtract one more each time
k 0.32, 0.064, 0.012 8 : ÷5   **l** 0.1875, 0.093 75, 0.046 875 : ÷2

▬ Homework 23C

1 a 4, 7, 10, 13, 16   **b** 1, 3, 5, 7, 9   **c** 6, 10, 14, 18, 22   **d** 2, 8, 18, 32, 50   **e** 0, 3, 8, 15, 24
2 a 3, 4, 5, 6, 7   **b** 3, 7, 11, 15, 19   **c** 1, 5, 9, 13, 17   **d** 2, 5, 10, 17, 26   **e** 3, 9, 19, 33, 51

▬ Homework 23D

1 a $2n + 3$ **b** $4n - 1$ **c** $5n + 1$ **d** $6n - 3$ **e** $3n + 1$ **f** $7n - 4$
2 a 101   **b** 201   **c** 253   **d** 296   **e** 152   **f** 345
3 a i $3n + 1$ **ii** 301   **iii** 100   **b i** $2n + 5$ **ii** 205   **iii** 99 or 101   **c i** $5n - 2$ **ii** 498   **iii** 98
d i $4n - 3$ **ii** 397   **iii** 101   **e i** $8n - 6$ **ii** 794   **iii** 98   **f i** $n + 4$ **ii** 104   **iii** 100

▬ Homework 23E

1 a 12   **b** $3n$ **c** 17
2 a

b $5n + 1$ **c** 126   **d** diagram 39

3 a

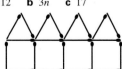

b $9n + 1$ **c** 541   **d** diagram 11

Intermediate Mathematics for GCSE: Answers

Chapter 1

Homework 1A

1 312 **2** 561 **3** 2268 **4** 2047 **5** 3074 **6** 2464 **7** 3760 **8** 9219 **9** 20 020 **10** 38 646

Homework 1B

1 24 **2** 32 **3** 41 **4** 36 **5** 31 **6** 19 **7** 23 **8** 17 **9** 23 rem 5 **10** 17 rem 49

Homework 1C

1 384 **2** 40 **3 a** £3584 **b** $30 \times 100 = 3000$ **4** 27 **5** £728 **6** £2264 **7** £14 **8** 1536 **9** 23
10 a £1000 **b** £912

Homework 1D

1 a 3 **b** 8 **c** 6 **d** $\frac{12}{15}$ **e** $\frac{4}{16}$ **f** $\frac{15}{40}$ **g** 4, 4, 24 **h** 3, 3, 30 **i** 5, 5, 35 **2 a** 10, 15, 15, 21, 33 **b** 18, 27, 16, 28, 36
3 a $\frac{2}{5}$ **b** $\frac{3}{4}$ **c** $\frac{3}{8}$ **d** $\frac{2}{9}$ **e** $\frac{9}{10}$ **4 a** $5 \div 8$ **b** $2 \div 5$ **c** $3 \div 7$ **d** $4 \div 9$ **e** $7 \div 10$

Homework 1E

1 a $3\frac{1}{5}$ **b** 4 **c** 3 **2 a** $2\frac{2}{3}$ **b** $\frac{2}{5}$ **c** $\frac{3}{8}$ **d** $\frac{9}{10}$ **e** $\frac{5}{7}$ **f** $\frac{7}{10}$ **3 a** $\frac{6}{7}$ **b** $\frac{5}{8}$ **c** $\frac{3}{4}$ **d** $\frac{1}{3}$
4 a < **b** > **c** > **d** < **e** > **f** > **g** < **h** > **i** = **j** > **k** = **l** < **m** < **n** > **o** < **p** >

Homework 1F

1 a $\frac{80}{5} = 16$ **b** $\frac{90}{6} = 15$ **c** $\frac{96}{4} = 24$ **d** $\frac{150}{10} = 15$ **2 a** 285 **b** 76 **c** 84 **d** 60 **3 a** $\frac{3}{5}$ of 70 **b** $\frac{2}{3}$ of 76 **4** 17.25
5 450 **6** 18 400 **7** 4000 **8** Seven eighths of sixteen million **9** They are equal.

Homework 1G

1 a $1\frac{3}{5}$ **b** $1\frac{1}{3}$ **c** $2\frac{1}{4}$ **d** $2\frac{7}{8}$ **e** $6\frac{1}{2}$ **f** $4\frac{1}{9}$ **g** $11\frac{1}{4}$ **h** $2\frac{1}{8}$ **i** $6\frac{3}{9}$ **j** $6\frac{8}{9}$ **k** $7\frac{1}{10}$ **l** $8\frac{3}{5}$
  m $9\frac{1}{6}$ **n** $5\frac{4}{9}$ **o** $2\frac{7}{12}$ **p** $5\frac{13}{15}$ **q** $13\frac{1}{4}$ **r** $10\frac{8}{9}$
2 a $\frac{11}{8}$ **b** $\frac{17}{3}$ **c** $\frac{22}{5}$ **d** $\frac{13}{8}$ **e** $\frac{15}{4}$ **f** $\frac{59}{6}$ **g** $\frac{37}{10}$ **h** $\frac{29}{8}$ **i** $\frac{99}{8}$ **j** $\frac{38}{5}$ **k** $\frac{19}{4}$ **l** $\frac{73}{10}$ **m** $\frac{29}{5}$ **n** $\frac{59}{8}$ **o** $\frac{18}{7}$ **p** $\frac{53}{10}$ **q** $\frac{69}{8}$ **r** $\frac{27}{8}$

Homework 1H

1 a $\frac{7}{10}$ **b** $\frac{5}{6}$ **c** $\frac{13}{30}$ **d** $\frac{17}{24}$ **e** $\frac{19}{20}$ **f** $\frac{11}{15}$ **g** $\frac{39}{40}$ **h** $\frac{9}{10}$ **2 a** $\frac{3}{4}$ **b** $\frac{1}{2}$ **c** $\frac{7}{10}$ **d** $\frac{7}{8}$
3 a $\frac{1}{8}$ **b** $\frac{3}{10}$ **c** $\frac{7}{15}$ **d** $\frac{7}{20}$ **4 a** $1\frac{3}{8}$ **b** $1\frac{1}{10}$ **c** $1\frac{1}{12}$ **d** $1\frac{5}{12}$ **5** $\frac{1}{2}$ **6** $\frac{1}{10}$ **7** 13 125 **8** 97

Homework 1 I

1 a $\frac{1}{3}$ **b** $\frac{3}{10}$ **c** $\frac{3}{10}$ **d** $\frac{2}{7}$ **e** $\frac{5}{9}$ **f** $\frac{1}{5}$ **g** $\frac{7}{15}$ **h** $\frac{3}{20}$ **i** $\frac{1}{6}$ **j** $\frac{7}{20}$
2 a 3 **b** $2\frac{1}{3}$ **c** 2 **d** $2\frac{1}{6}$ **e** $5\frac{1}{5}$ **f** $4\frac{2}{3}$ **g** $4\frac{1}{12}$ **h** 12 **3** $2\frac{1}{4}$ km **4** $\frac{2}{5}$ **5** $4\frac{3}{5}$ kg **6** $\frac{2}{3}$ of $4\frac{2}{5} = 2\frac{14}{15}$ **7** 66 litres

Homework 1J

1 a $\frac{3}{5}$ **b** $1\frac{3}{5}$ **c** $1\frac{1}{5}$ **d** $\frac{9}{14}$ **e** $2\frac{2}{3}$ **f** $1\frac{4}{7}$ **g** $4\frac{4}{7}$ **h** $4\frac{4}{5}$ **i** $4\frac{1}{8}$ **j** $2\frac{13}{16}$ **k** $1\frac{1}{4}$ **l** $\frac{64}{75}$
2 48 **3** 15 **4** 80 **5 a** $\frac{3}{20}$ **b** $\frac{7}{16}$ **c** $\frac{1}{2}$ **d** 1 **e** $\frac{25}{33}$ **f** 1

Homework 1K

1 a $-2°$ **b** $-3°$ **c** $-4°$ **d** $-3°$ **e** $-2°$ **f** $-3°$ **g** 4 **h** 3 **i** -3 **j** -5 **k** 2 **l** 4 **m** -10 **n** -8
  o -6 **p** -3 **q** -5 **r** -4 **s** 4 **t** -1 **u** -7 **v** -3 **w** -2 **x** -6
2 a -5 **b** -2 **c** -10 **d** 4 **e** 8 **f** -3 **g** 6 **h** 12 **i** -8 **j** -11 **k** 11 **l** 36 **m** -42 **n** -32
  o -25 **p** 4 **q** -14 **r** 9 **s** -56 **t** -11 **u** 38 **v** 15 **w** -40 **x** -202
3 a 5 **b** -5 **c** 7 **d** -5 **e** -4 **f** -7 **g** -9 **h** 1 **i** -3

Homework 1L

1 a -8 **b** -18 **c** -35 **d** 12 **e** 16 **f** 7 **g** 4 **h** -5 **i** 2 **j** 2 **k** -21 **l** -18 **m** -28 **n** -27 **o** 14
  p -7 **q** -4 **r** -5 **s** 5 **t** -25 **u** 24 **v** -7 **w** -63 **x** 6 **y** -56
2 a 2 **b** 3 **c** 2 **d** -7 **e** -10 **f** -12 **g** -12 **h** 30 **i** -8 **j** -4 **k** -4 **l** 3 **m** 3 **n** -12 **o** -9
  p 32 **q** 15 **r** -48 **s** -12 **t** 52 **u** -11 **v** 48 **w** -2 **x** -20 **y** 1
3 a -5 **b** 6 **c** -10 **d** 20 **e** -15

Homework 1M

1 a 30 **b** 70 **c** 20 **d** 50 **e** 60 **f** 10 **g** 100 **h** 120 **i** 110 **j** 130
2 a 200 **b** 400 **c** 400 **d** 800 **e** 900 **f** 100 **g** 600 **h** 300 **i** 1000 **j** 1200
3 a 2000 **b** 4000 **c** 7000 **d** 4000 **e** 1000 **f** 7000 **g** 6000 **h** 9000 **i** 2000 **j** 10 000
4 a 15 **b** 30 **c** 35 **d** 40 **e** 25 **f** 20 **5** 8000, 13 000, 45 000, 76 000, 100 000 **6 a** 235 **b** 244.99
7 a 7500 **b** 8499

Homework 1N

1 a 3.7 **b** 8.7 **c** 5.3 **d** 18.8 **e** 0.4 **f** 26.3 **g** 3.8 **h** 10.1 **i** 11.1 **j** 12.0
2 a 6.72 **b** 4.46 **c** 1.97 **d** 3.49 **e** 5.81 **f** 2.56 **g** 21.80 **h** 12.99 **i** 2.30 **j** 5.56
3 a 0.09 **b** 4.56 **c** 2.10 **d** 0.763 **e** 7.1 **f** 8.90 **g** 23.781 **h** 1.0
4 a 7 **b** 9 **c** 3 **d** 8 **e** 8 **f** 3 **g** 2 **h** 2 **i** 5 **j** 4

Homework 1P

1 a 50 000 **b** 60 000 **c** 30 000 **d** 90 000 **e** 90 000 **f** 50 **g** 90 **h** 30 **i** 100 **j** 200 **k** 0.5 **l** 0.3
m 0.006 **n** 0.05 **o** 0.0009 **p** 10 **q** 90 **r** 90 **s** 200 **t** 1000
2 Hellaby 850 to 949 Hook 645 to 654 Hundleton 1045 to 1054
3 a 6700 **b** 36 000 **c** 69 000 **d** 42 000 **e** 27 000 **f** 7000 **g** 2200 **h** 960 **i** 440 **j** 330
4 a 50 000 **b** 6200 **c** 89.7 **d** 220 **e** 8 **f** 1.1 **g** 730 **h** 6000 **i** 67 **j** 6 **k** 8 **l** 9.75 **m** 26
n 30 **o** 870 **p** 40 **q** 0.085 **r** 0.0099 **s** 0.08 **t** 0.0620

Homework 1Q

1 a 28 000 **b** 42 000 **c** 210 **d** 20 000 **e** 2000 **f** 2100 **g** 5 **h** 9 **i** 700 **j** 75 **k** 50 **l** 8
2 a £4000 **b** £2000 **c** £1500 **3 a** £30 000 **b** £36 000 **4** 6 litres **5** £1400 **6** 20p
7 a 105 km **b** 450 km **c** 5000 km

Homework 1R

1 a 1.62 m **b** 20 minutes **c** 3 kg **d** 1.24°C **e** 24 000 **2** 25 jars **3** 65 minutes to 2 sf
4 a £2630 to 3 sf **b** £604 to 3 sf **c** £86.30 to 3 sf **5** 62 mph **6** £217

Chapter 2

Homework 2A

1 a $\frac{1}{10}$ **b** $\frac{2}{5}$ **c** $\frac{1}{4}$ **d** $\frac{3}{20}$ **e** $\frac{3}{4}$ **f** $\frac{7}{20}$ **g** $\frac{3}{25}$ **h** $\frac{7}{25}$ **i** $\frac{14}{25}$ **j** $\frac{9}{50}$ **k** $\frac{21}{50}$ **l** $\frac{3}{50}$
2 a 0.87 **b** 0.25 **c** 0.33 **d** 0.05 **e** 0.01 **f** 0.72 **g** 0.58 **h** 0.175 **i** 0.085 **j** 0.682 **k** 1.5 **l** 1.32
3

Percentage	Fraction	Decimal
10%	$\frac{1}{10}$	0.1
20%	$\frac{2}{10} = \frac{1}{5}$	0.2
30%	$\frac{3}{10}$	0.3
40%	$\frac{4}{10} = \frac{2}{5}$	0.4
50%	$\frac{5}{10} = \frac{1}{2}$	0.5
60%	$\frac{6}{10} = \frac{3}{5}$	0.6
70%	$\frac{7}{10}$	0.7
80%	$\frac{8}{10} = \frac{4}{5}$	0.8
90%	$\frac{9}{10}$	0.9

4 55% **5** 16% **6** 23% **7** 69%
8 a $\approx 20\%$ **b** $\approx 75\%$ **c** $\approx 90\%$

Homework 2B

1 a £50 **b** £12 **c** 212 kg **d** 63 cm **e** £18.48 **f** 177.5 g **g** £0.72 **h** 304 m **i** £2.52 **j** £9.80 **k** 13.6 *l*
l £297.60
2 208 **3** Y7 240, Y8 230, Y9 210, Y10 220, Y11 200 **4** 378*t*, 63*t*, 9*t* **5 a** £7 **b** £14.35 **c** £42 **6** £600

Homework 2C

1 a £84 **b** £165 **c** 920 m **d** 400 kg **e** £54.60 **f** £39.60 **g** 141.6 cm **h** £46.72 **i** 1017.5 g **j** £123.84
2 £33 800 **3** £54.18, £42.14, £109.32, £5.47, £114.79 **4 a** £2160 **b** £2320 **c** £2480
5 clock: £21.15, wallet: £17.86, towel: £15.04, bookmark: £7.52

Homework 2D

1 a £7.68 **b** 15.98 kg **c** 235.2 m **2 a** 324 g **b** 374 m **c** 270 cm **3** £7392 **4** 64 **5** 7
6 a 450 g **b** 550 g **7** 680 units

Homework 2E

1 a 5.5 cm **b** 6.05 cm **c** 7.32 cm **d** 9.74 cm **2 a** £32 413.50 **b** 7 years **3 a** £291.60 **b** £314.93 **c** £367.33
4 a 1725 **b** 1984 **c** 2624
5 After 11 years the sycamore is 93.26 cm tall and the conifer is 93.05 cm tall.
After 12 years the sycamore is 100.73 cm tall and the conifer is 107 cm tall.

Homework 2F

1 a 20% **b** 25% **c** 10% **d** 75% **e** 80% **f** 46% **g** 33.3% **h** 30% **i** 67.5% **j** 23.8%
2 a 75% **b** 37.5% **3 a** 60% **b** 40% **4** 29.3% **5 a** 66.7% **b** 50% **c** 50.0% **d** 66.6%

Homework 2G

1 a 800 g **b** 96 m **c** 840 cm **2 a** 70 kg **b** £180 **c** 40 hours **3** Jumper £12 Socks £1.60 Trousers £20
4 £15 **5** £180 **6** £50 **7** 800 g **8** 550 CDs

Chapter 3

Homework 3A

1 a 1:3 **b** 1:5 **c** 1:6 **d** 1:3 **e** 2:3 **f** 3:5 **g** 5:8 **h** 15:2 **i** 2:5 **j** 5:2
2 a 1:4 **b** 3:4 **c** 1:8 **d** 2:5 **e** 2:5 **f** 8:15 **g** 10:3 **h** 1:3 **i** 3:8 **j** 1:5
3 a $\frac{1}{4}$ **b** $\frac{3}{4}$ **4 a** $\frac{2}{5}$ **b** $\frac{3}{5}$ **5 a** $\frac{1}{10}$ **b** $\frac{9}{10}$

Homework 3B

1 a £2:£8 **b** £4:£8 **c** £10:£30 **d** 10 g:50 g **e** 1 h:9 h **f** 10 kg:15 kg
   g 18 days:12 days **h** 30 m:40 m **i** £1.50:£3.50 **j** 15 h:9 h
2 a 300 **b** 100 **3** 2 m and 18 m **4** 400 **5** 45 **6** £6 **7** £30 and £36
8 a 1:1.5 **b** 1:2.5 **c** 1:1.25 **d** 1:1.6 **e** 1:2.1

Homework 3C

1 20 **2** 80 **3 a** 15 *l* **b** 25 *l* **4 a** 80 kg **b** 5 kg **5** 90 **6 a** 200 g **b** 320 g **7 a** £4000 **b** £6000

Homework 3D

1 15 mph **2** 180 miles **3** 46 mph **4** 2pm
5 a 30 mph **b** 50 km/h **c** 20 miles **d** 50 km **e** 3 hours 15 minutes **f** 3 hours 36 minutes
6 a 130 km **b** 52 km/h **7 a** 30 minutes **b** 12 mph **8 a** 1.25 h **b** 45 miles

Homework 3E

1 0.9 g/cm^3 **2** 62.5 g/cm^3 **3** 30 g **4** 389 cm^3 **5** 1350 g **6** 909 cm^3 **7** 5.25 g/cm^3 **8** 996 Tonnes **9** 1.11 g/cm^3

Chapter 4

Homework 4A

1

	Length	Breadth	Perimeter	Area
a	8 cm	5 cm	26 cm	40 cm^2
b	10 cm	8 cm	36 cm	80 cm^2
c	9 cm	3 cm	24 cm	27 cm^2

2 a Perimeter = 38 cm, Area = 64 cm^2 **b** Perimeter = 78 cm, Area = 184 cm^2 **3 a** 180 m **b** 1800 m^2 **4** 28 cm **5** 114.3 *l*

Homework 4B

1 a 9.4 cm **b** 31.4 cm **c** 50.3 m **d** 44.0 cm **e** 20.1 cm **f** 22.0 cm **2** 200 π **3 a** 15.7 cm **b** 2 **4** 18.0 cm
5 6π + 12 **6** 1700 revs **7** 3.82 cm

Homework 4C

1 a Area = 84 cm^2, Perimeter = 56 cm **b** Area = 330 cm^2, Perimeter = 132 cm **2 a** 13 cm^2 **b** 95 cm^2
3 a 22.5 m^2 **b** 101 m^2 **4** 10 cm

Homework 4D

1 a 35 cm^2 **b** 6 cm **c** 8 cm **2 a** 130 cm^2 **b** 78 cm^2 **3 a** 70 cm^2 **b** 59 cm^2
4 1 = Base = 60, Height = 2, 2 = Base = 30, Height = 4, 3 = Base = 15, Height = 8, 4 = Base = 12, Height = 10,
   5 = Base = 24, Height = 5, 6 = Base = 20, Height = 6
5 1 = Base = 20, Height = 10, 2 = Base = 50, Height = 4, 3 = Base = 40, Height = 5, 4 = Base = 100, Height = 2,
   5 = Base = 25, Height 8, 6 = Base = 200, Height = 1
6 The Height

Homework 4E

1 a 23.1 cm   28 cm^2 **b** 36 cm   66.5 cm^2 **2 a** 89 m^2 **b** 35.5 cm^2 **3 a** 45 cm^2 **b** 24 cm^2
4 a is 10 cm^2 and **b** is 9.6 cm^2 **5** 64.7%

Homework 4F

1 a 16π cm^2 **b** 153.9 cm^2 **c** 254.5 cm^2 **d** π m^2 **e** 1385.4 cm^2 **f** 0.6 cm^2 **2** 66 m^2 **3** 88.4 cm^2 **4** 3.99 m
5 49.7 cm^2 **6** 329 m^2

Exercise 4G

1 a 7π cm   **b** 10π cm   **c** 19π cm   **d** 6π cm   **2 a** 64π cm   **b** 12.25π cm   **c** 81π cm   **d** 20.25π cm   **3** 4 cm
4 5 cm   **5** $\frac{20}{\pi}$ **6** $\sqrt{\frac{20}{\pi}}$ **7 a** $\frac{12}{\sqrt{\pi}}$ **b** $\frac{7}{\sqrt{\pi}}$ **c** $\frac{1.44}{\sqrt{\pi}}$

Chapter 5

Homework 5A

1 a i 72 cm^3 **ii** 108 cm^2 **b i** 100 cm^3 **ii** 160 cm^2 **c i** 180 cm^3 **ii** 222 cm^2 **d i** 125 cm^3 **ii** 150 cm^2
2 24 cm^3, 5 cm, 5 cm, 6 cm   **3** 90 m^3 **4 a** 60 cm^3 **b** 160 cm^3 **c** 120 cm^3 **5** 24   **6 a** 544 cm^3 **b** 225 m^3

Homework 5B

1 a 549.78 cm^3 **b** 2513.27 cm^3 **c** 2261.95 cm^3 **d** 572.56 cm^3 **2 a** 753.98 cm^3 **b** 117.81 cm^3 **c** 1460.06 cm^3
3 4021.24 g   **4** 3.09 cm   **5** 62 731 322 g   **6** 6 250 000 cm   **7 a** 176π cm^3 **b** 1152π cm

Homework 5C

1 a 10.5 cm^2 42 cm^3 **b** 25 cm^2 250 cm^3 **2 i** 190 g   **ii** 187.8 g   **iii** 189 g

Chapter 6

Homework 6A

1 a $x + 4$ **b** $x - 7$ **c** $3 + k$ **d** $8 - t$ **e** $x + y$ **f** $4x$ **g** $5t$ **h** ab **i** $\frac{m}{2}$ **j** $\frac{p}{q}$

2 a $3a$ **b** $5b$ **c** $9c$ **d** $4d$ **e** $3e$ **f** $8f$ **g** 0 **h** $-2h$ **i** $5i^2$ **j** $4j^2$
3 a $8x + 3y$ **b** $2m + 10p$ **c** $6x + 4$ **d** $5 + 3x$ **e** $8p$ **f** $6x - 2$ **g** $2p - 6$ **h** $6x - 2y$ **i** $7 + 6p - 3t$ **j** $6w - 4k$
4 a $2a + 8$ **b** $3b - 9$ **c** $5c + 5$ **d** $4e + 10$ **e** $12e - 4$ **f** $25m + 35$ **g** $10a + 4b$ **h** $6x - 8y$ **i** $12p + 3q$
  j $a^2 + 3a$ **k** $b^2 - 2b$ **l** $2x^2 + 5x$
5 a $x + 4$ **b** $x - 5$ **6 a** $3n$ **b** $n + 2$ **c** $2n + 5$ **7 a** Frank $p + 2$, Chloe $p - 3$, Lizzie $2p$

8 a £4   **b** £$(10 - a)$ **c** £$(b - c)$ **9 a** 21   **b** $7z$ **10 a** £10   **b** £$\frac{r}{4}$ **c** £$\frac{p}{q}$

Homework 6B

1 a 7   **b** 13   **c** 23   **2 a** 2   **b** 14   **c** 32   **3 a** 8   **b** 24   **c** $4\frac{1}{2}$ **4 a** 4   **b** 0   **c** -2
5 a 35   **b** 60   **c** 85   **6 a** 10   **b** 28   **c** 1   **7 a** 2   **b** 3   **c** 5   **8 a** 1   **b** 4   **c** $5\frac{1}{2}$ **9 a** 10   **b** 2   **c** 1
10 a 21   **b** 33   **c** 45

Homework 6C

1 a 16   **b** 16   **c** 1.21   **2 a** 25   **b** 169   **3 a** 16   **b** 21   **4 a** 51   **b** 36   **c** 19   **5 a** 17   **b** 28
6 a -14 **b** 25   **c** -50 **7 a** 624   **b** 217   **8 a** 102   **b** 791

Homework 6D

1 1.8   **2** 8.5   **3** 16.5   **4** $\frac{23}{3}$ **5** 0.75   **6** $\frac{10}{3}$ **7** 4   **8** $\frac{8}{9}$ **9** $\frac{19}{3}$ **10** $\frac{60}{7}$ **11** 6.5   **12** 4.4   **13** $\frac{13}{3}$
14 0.75   **15** $\frac{8}{3}$ **16** $\frac{16}{7}$ **17** 1.4   **18** $\frac{19}{4}$ **19** 23.5   **20** $\frac{5}{9}$ **21** $\frac{4}{3}$ **22** $\frac{9}{5}$ **23** 2   **24** 1.5

Homework 6E

1 12   **2** 12   **3** 35   **4** 24   **5** 35   **6** 20   **7** 4   **8** 32   **9** 18   **10** 28   **11** 54   **12** 64   **13** 6   **14** 6.4
15 18.75   **16** 12   **17** 4.2   **18** $\frac{40}{3}$ **19** $-\frac{7}{8}$ **20** $-\frac{8}{5}$

Homework 6F

1 -0.5 **2** -0.8 **3** $-\frac{7}{4}$ **4** -5.5 **5** -0.8 **6** $-\frac{11}{8}$ **7** $-\frac{15}{4}$ **8** -0.4 **9** 1   **10** -2 **11** 18   **12** 15   **13** 8
14 -0.6 **15** 5.75   **16** $\frac{17}{8}$ **17** -0.6 **18** -4 **19** -2.75 **20** -1.5

Homework 6G

1 −1 **2** 10 **3** 2 **4** 1.5 **5** 2.4 **6** 3.1 **7** 6.75 **8** 3 **9** $-\frac{5}{12}$ **10** 2.6 **11** 2.1 **12** $-\frac{2}{3}$ **13** 2.8 **14** 4
15 7.25 **16** $\frac{11}{6}$ **17** −5.25 **18** −3 **19** −0.6 **20** $\frac{59}{12}$ **21** 0.1 **22** −2.5 **23** $\frac{23}{24}$ **24** −2

Homework 6H

1 a 2 and 3 **b** 3 and 4 **c** 9 and 10 **d** 6 and 7 **2 a** 2.9 **b** 4.6 **c** 7.9 **d** 5.8
3 a 1 and 2 **b** 3 and 4 **c** 4 and 5 **d** 4 and 5 **4 a** 3.2 **b** 4.6 **c** 5.4 **d** 7.0 **5** 3.5 **6** 4.7

Homework 6 I

1 10.7 and 18.7 cm **2** 21.8 and 36.8 m **3** 5.4 and 7.4 cm **4** 12.6 and 9.6 cm **5** 7.9 **6** 3.5 **7** 2.8

Chapter 7

Homework 7A

1 a 25° **b** 35° **c** 55° **d** 84° **e** 85° **f** 145° **g** 168° **h** 200°

Homework 7B

1 a 55° **b** 147° **c** 40° **2 a** $x = 42°, y = 138°$ **b** $x = 111°, y = 69°$ **c** $x = 80°, y = 100°$ **3 a** 25° **b** 75° **c** 155°
4 a 70° **b** 135°

Homework 7C

1 a $a = 60°$ **b** $b = 50°$ **c** $c = 152°$ **d** $d = e = 62°$ **e** $f = g = 115°$ **f** $h = i = 72°$
2 a $a = b = c = 55°$ **b** $d = 132°, e = 48°$ **c** $f = 78°, g = 102°$ **3 a** 70° **b** 68°

Homework 7D

1 a 900° **b** 1620° **c** 3240° **d** 5940° **2 a** 156° **b** 160° **c** 168° **d** 176.4° **3 a** 10 **b** 16 **c** 36 **d** 40
4 a 18 **b** 12 **c** 20 **d** 90 **5 a** 8 **b** 24 **c** 36 **d** 15 **6** Octagon **7 a** Decagon **b** 115°

Homework 7E

1 a 55° **b** $c = 70°, d = 40°$ **c** $e = 64°, f = 52°$ **d** $g = 52.5°, h = 52.5°$ **2 a** 70° **b** 55° **c** 57.5° **3** N/A
4 64°, 58° and 58° **5** 120°, 30° and 30° **6 a** 140° **b** 20° **c** 120° **7 a** 144° **b** 126° **c** 108°

Homework 7F

1 a $a = 110°, b = 100°$ **b** $c = 68°, d = 108°$ **c** $e = 90°, f = 105°$
2 a $a = c = 130°, b = 50°$ **b** $d = f = 45°, e = 135°$ **c** $g = i = 139°, h = 41°$
3 a $a = 120°, b = 50°$ **b** $c = d = 90°$ **c** $e = 96°, f = 56°$
4 a $a = c = 125°, b = 55°$ **b** $d = f = 70°, e = 110°$ **c** $g = i = 117°, h = 63°$ **5** $x = 50°, y = 40°, x = 11°, y = 40°$
6 a $x = 100°$, Trapezium **b** $x = 50°$, Kite **7 a** 360

Chapter 8

Homework 8A

1 a Yes SAS **b** Yes SSS **c** Yes ASA

Homework 8B

1 i $\binom{7}{1}$ **ii** $\binom{10}{-2}$ **iii** $\binom{3}{-2}$ **iv** $\binom{-7}{-1}$ **v** $\binom{3}{-3}$ **vi** $\binom{-4}{-3}$ **3 a** $\binom{1}{-5}$ **b** $\binom{-8}{6}$ **c** $\binom{1}{-5}$ **d** $\binom{6}{4}$ **e** $\binom{7}{-1}$ **f** $\binom{7}{-1}$ **g** $\binom{8}{-6}$ **h** $\binom{-6}{-4}$

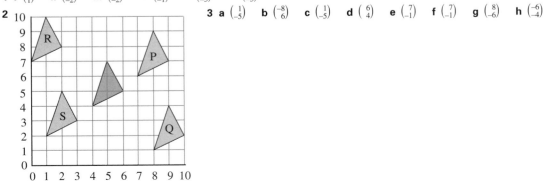

Homework 8C

1 a 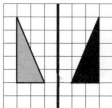 **b** 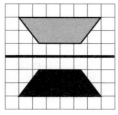 **c** 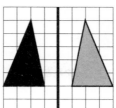 **d**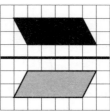

2 a 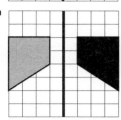 **b** 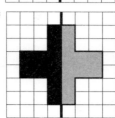 **c** 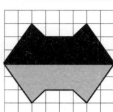 **d**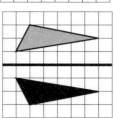

3 a and b

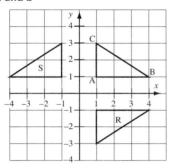

4 a, b, c, d and e

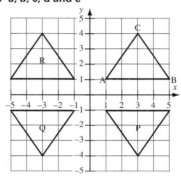

3 c congruent

4 f a reflection in the *y*-axis

Homework 8D

1 a 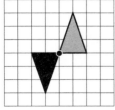 **b** 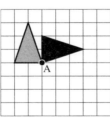 **c** 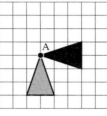 **d**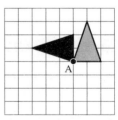

2 a 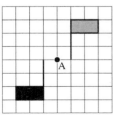 **b** 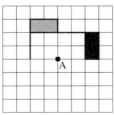 **c** 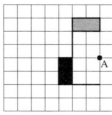 **d**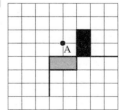

3 a, b and c

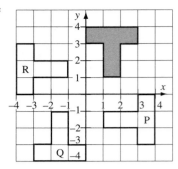

3 d a rotation of 90° clockwise about O

4 a A(1, 1), B(3, 1), C(3, 3), D(1, 3)
  b, c, d

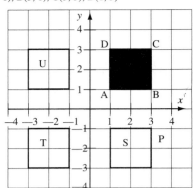

4 e corresponding vertices have same pairs of coordinates switching round and changing signs

▬ Homework 8F

1 a reflection in x-axis   **b** reflection in y-axis   **c** translation of $\binom{6}{-1}$ **d** rotation of 180° (anti-)clockwise about (0, 0)

e rotation of 90° clockwise about (0, 0)   **f** reflection in y = −x   **g** reflection in y = x

2 e 90° clockwise about (0, 0)   **3** (−5, −2)

Chapter 9

▬ Homework 9A

1 a 210°   **b** 255°   **c** 290°   **d** 340°   **e** 025°   **f** 50°   **g** 100°   **h** 140°
3 035°
4 a Fly due north for n meters, then turn to bearing 240° and travel for n meters, then turn to bearing 120° and continue until back at beginning or he could fly north for n meters, then turn to bearing 120°, carry on for n meters then turn to bearing 240° and carry on until back at start.
  b Head on 070° for n meters, then turn to bearing 190° and carry on for n meters, then turn to bearing 310° and carry on until at beginning or carry on along 070° for n meters, then turn 100°, carry on for n meters, then turn to bearing 190° and carry on until back at beginning.

▬ Homework 9B

4 b rhombus

▬ Homework 9C

5

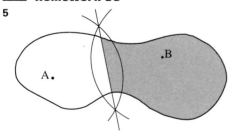

▬ Homework 9D

5 e AC = 5.9 cm, BC = 7.2 cm   **6 b** BC = 3 cm

Chapter 10

▬ Homework 10A

1

Shape	Line of symmetry	Rotational symmetry
Rectangle	2	2
Regular pentagon	5	5
Race track	2	2
Isosceles triangle with one angle 90°	1	1
Parallelogram	0	2
Arc of a circle	1	1
3, 4, 5 triangle	0	1

2 Only **b** and **d** are impossible

3 Only **c** is impossible

4 No you cannot, because shapes with 2 lines of symmetry will have rotational symmetry of order 2, shapes with 4 lines of symmetry will have rotational symmetry of order 4, etc.

▬ Homework 10B

3 a i 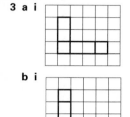   **ii**   **iii**

b i 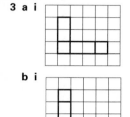   **ii**   **iii**

▬ Homework 10C

1 c thousands   **2 c** thousands   **3 a** 0   **b** 1   **c** 0

▬ Homework 10D

1 a 6 planes of symmetry and one axis of rotational symmetry   **b** 10 planes of symmetry and one axis of rotational symmetry.

2 a 3   **b** an infinite number   **c** 1   **d** 1   **e** probably 2   **f** 1   **5** 6

Chapter 11

▬ Homework 11A

1 a 4, 8, 12, 16, 20   **b** 6, 12, 18, 24, 30   **c** 8, 16, 24, 32, 40   **d** 12, 24, 36, 48, 60   **e** 15, 30, 45, 60, 75

2 a 28, 36, 64, 56, 60   **b** 15, 45, 60   **c** 64, 56   **d** 77, 66

3 a 252, 161, 224, 378, 315, 182   **b** 225, 252, 297, 162, 378, 315, 369   **c** 252, 312

4 a 198   **b** 196   **c** 195   **d** 192   **e** 198   **5 a** 12   **b** 102   **c** 1002   **d** 10 002   **e** 1 000 000 002

▬ Homework 11B

3 7   **8** 30

▬ Homework 11C

1 a 5^4 **b** 7^5 **c** 19^3 **d** 4^5 **e** 1^7 **f** 8^5 **g** 6^1 **h** 11^6 **i** 0.9^4 **j** 999^3

2 a $4 \times 4 \times 4 \times 4 \times 4$ **b** $8 \times 8 \times 8 \times 8$ **c** $5 \times 5 \times 5$ **d** $9 \times 9 \times 9 \times 9 \times 9 \times 9$ **e** $1 \times 1 \times 1 \times 1 \times 1 \times 1 \times 1 \times 1 \times 1 \times 1 \times 1$
f $7 \times 7 \times 7$ **g** $5.2 \times 5.2 \times 5.2$ **h** $7.5 \times 7.5 \times 7.5$ **i** $7.7 \times 7.7 \times 7.7 \times 7.7$ **j** $10\,000 \times 10\,000 \times 10\,000$

3 a 625   **b** 16 807   **c** 6859   **d** 1024   **e** 1   **f** 32 768   **g** 6   **h** 1 771 561   **i** 0.6561   **j** 997 002 999

4 a 1024   **b** 4096   **c** 125   **d** 531 441   **e** 1   **f** 343   **g** 140.608   **h** 421.875   **i** 3515.3041   **j** 1 000 000 000 000

5 a 1   **b** 9   **c** 1   **d** 1   **e** 100 000   **6 a** −8   **b** −1   **c** 81   **d** −125   **e** 1 000 000

7 a 16   **b** −125   **c** 81   **d** −32   **e** 1

▬ Homework 11D

1 a 7^5 **b** 7^9 **c** 7^7 **d** 7^6 **e** 7^{14} **f** 7^8 **2 a** 5^4 **b** 5^6 **c** 5^1 **d** 5^0 **e** 5^2

3 a a^3 **b** a^5 **c** a^7 **d** a^4 **e** a^2 **f** a **4 a** $15a^6$ **b** $21a^5$ **c** $30a^6$ **d** $12a^9$ **e** $125a^8$

5 a $4a^3$ **b** $3a^5$ **c** $5a^5$ **d** $8a^9$ **e** $3a^8$ **f** $6a^{-4}$ **6 a** $12a^6b^3$ **b** $14a^4b^8$ **c** $20a^7b^4$ **d** $3a^2b^4$ **e** $4ab^8$

7 Let $x = 0$ and $y = 1$, so $a^0 \div a^1 = \dfrac{1}{a} = a^{0-1} = a^{-1}$

Homework 11E

1 a 350 **b** 21.5 **c** 6740 **d** 46.3 **e** 301.45 **f** 78 560 **g** 642 **h** 0.67 **i** 85 **j** 79 800 **k** 658 **l** 21 530
m 889 000 **n** 35 214.7 **o** 37 284.1 **p** 34 280 000
2 a 45.38 **b** 43.5 **c** 76.459 **d** 64.37 **e** 42.287 **f** 0.2784 **g** 2.465 **h** 7.63 **i** 0.076 **j** 0.008 97
k 0.0865 **l** 0.015 **m** 0.000 000 879 9 **n** 0.234 **o** 7.654 **p** 0.000 073 2
3 a 120 000 **b** 200 000 **c** 14 000 **d** 21 000 **e** 900 **f** 125 000 **g** 40 000 **h** 6000 **i** 14 000 **j** 300 000
k 7500 **l** 140 000
4 a 5 **b** 300 **c** 35 **d** 40 **e** 3 **f** 150 **g** 14 **h** 50 **i** 6 **j** 15 **k** 4 **l** 200
5 a 730 **b** 329 000 **c** 7940 **d** 68 000 000 **e** 0.034 6 **f** 0.000 507 **g** 0.000 23 **h** 0.000 89

Homework 11F

1 a 350 **b** 41.5 **c** 0.005 7 **d** 14.6 **e** 0.038 9 **f** 4600 **g** 270 **h** 86 **i** 4600 **j** 397 000 **k** 0.003 65
l 705
2 a 7.8×10^2 **b** 4.35×10^{-1} **c** 6.78×10^4 **d** 7.4×10^9 **e** 3.078×10^{10} **f** 4.278×10^{-4} **g** 6.45×10^3
h 4.7×10^2 **i** 1.2×10^{-4} **j** 9.643×10^1 **k** 7.478×10 **l** 4.1578×10^{-3}
3 $1.99 \times 10^3, 2.4673 \times 10^7$ **4** $2.001 \times 10^3, 1.5282 \times 10^4$ **5** $1.99 \times 10^3, 6.13 \times 10^{11}$ **6** $9.3 \times 10^7, 2.4 \times 10^{13}$ **7** 6.5×10^{-13}

Homework 11g

1 a 3.6×10^{15} **b** 4.2×10^{11} **c** 2.1×10^{14} **d** 4.26×10^{15} **e** 5.4×10^{11} **f** 4.2×10^{10} **g** 1.8×10^{11} **h** 2.7×10^{31}
i 2.7×10^3 **j** 4.2×10^5
2 a 3×10^4 **b** 1.89×10^3 **c** 7×10^4 **d** 1.5×10^{-13} **e** 1.7×10^8 **f** 7.78×10^{14} **g** 1.37×10^3 **h** 6×10^4 **i**
3.67×10^4 **j** 1.03×10^{-2}
3 a 2×10^2 **b** 5×10^3 **c** 8×10^{11} **d** 2×10^9 **e** 5×10^{-1} **f** 5×10^2
4 a 7×10^{13} **b** 7×10^{-1} **c** 1.7×10^7 **d** 3×10^6 **e** 1.43

Chapter 12

Homework 12A

1 $x = 3, y = 2$ **2** $x = 5, y = 1$ **3** $x = 3, y = 2$ **4** $x = 5, y = -0.5$ **5 a** $x + y = 16, x - y = 9$ **b** $x = 12.5, y = 3.5$

Homework 12B

1 $x = 2, y = 3$ **2** $x = 7, y = 3$ **3** $x = 2, y = 5$ **4** $x = 4, y = 3$ **5 a** $4x + 3y = 335, 3x + y = 220,$ **b** $x = 65, y = 25, £4.25$

Homework 12C

1 $x = 3, y = 1$ **2** $x = 7, y = 2$ **3** $x = 2.5, y = 3$ **4** $x = 7, y = -1$
5 a $2x + 3y = 2850, 3x + 2y = 3150$ **b** $x = £7.50, y = £4.50$

Homework 12D

1 $x = 3, y = -2$ **2** $x = 2.5, y = -0.5$ **3** $x = 5, y = -3$ **4** $x = 2.5, y = -1$ **5** $x = -3, y = 5.5$ **6** $x = 0.2, y = 1.1$
7 $x = 2.5, y = 1.25$ **8** $x = 1.2, y = 0.2$ **9 a** $x + y = 50, 3x + 4.5y = 183$ **b** 28 @ £3 and 22 @ £4.50

Homework 12E

1 CD £10.50, book £3.50 **2** £1.91 **3** £1.21 **4** 11.5 kg **5** 12 g in cakes and 13 g in peanuts **6** £816.25

Homework 12F

1 a $x < 5$ **b** $t > 8$ **c** $p \geq 8$ **d** $x < 3$ **e** $y \leq 6$ **f** $t > 9$ **g** $x < 13$ **h** $y \leq 11$ **i** $t \geq 37$ **j** $x < 10$ **k** $x \leq 2$
l $t \geq \frac{7}{4}$ **m** $x \geq -6$ **n** $t \leq 4$ **o** $y \leq 6$ **p** $x \geq \frac{1}{2}$ **q** $w \leq 3.5$ **r** $x \leq \frac{5}{8}$
2 a 5, 4, 3, 2, 1 **b** no answer **c** 25, 16, 9, 4, 1 **d** 5, 3, 1 **e** 7, 5, 3, 2
3 a $2 < x < 3$ **b** $1 < x < 4$ **c** $-2 < x < 4$ **d** $2 \leq x < \frac{19}{3}$ **e** $3.5 \leq x < 7.5$ **f** $\frac{1}{2} \leq x < 3.75$ **g** $2 \leq x \leq 4$ **h** $\frac{5}{2} \leq x < 8$
i $\frac{4}{5} \leq x < 4.2$

Homework 12G

1 a $x \geq 1$ **b** $x < 2$ **c** $x \geq -2$ **d** $x \leq 0$ **e** $x > -5$ **f** $x \geq -1$

2

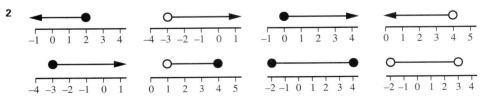

3 a $x \geq 4$ **b** $x < -2$ **c** $x \leq 5$ **d** $x > 3$ **e** $x \leq 1.5$ **f** $x \geq 4$ **g** $x > 7$ **h** $x < -1$ **i** $x < 2$ **j** $x \leq 3$ **k** $x > 24$
l $x \geq -2$
4 a $x > \frac{4}{5}$ **b** $x \leq 3$ **c** $x \geq \frac{19}{4}$ **d** $x < 6.5$ **e** $x \leq \frac{1}{2}$ **f** $x > -\frac{2}{5}$ **g** $x \geq -7$ **h** $x \leq -\frac{2}{5}$

Homework 12H

1 $-3 \le x \le 3$ **2** $x < -6, x > 6$ **3** $-10 < x < 10$ **4** $x \le -2, x \ge 2$ **5** $x \le -5, x \ge 5$ **6** $x < -4, x > 4$ **7** $-3 \le x \le 3$
8 All values **9** $x < -1, x > 1$ **10** $x \le -5, x \ge 5$ **11** $x < -4, x > 4$ **12** $-3 < x < 3$ **13** $-\sqrt{2.8} \le x \le \sqrt{2.8}$
14 $-4 < x < 4$ **15** $x \le -5, x \ge 5$ **16** $x \le -12, x \ge 12$ **17** $-0.4 < x < 0.4$ **18** $x \le -1.1, x \ge 1.1$ **19** $-\sqrt{93} \le x \le \sqrt{93}$ **20** $x < -0.5, x > 0.5$

Chapter 13

Homework 13A

1 a i mode 6, median 4, mean 4 **ii** mode 15, median 15, mean 15.1 **iii** mode 32, median 32, mean 33
  b i mean, balanced data **ii** mode, appears 6 times **iii** median, 46 is an extreme value
2 a mode 135 g, median 141 g, mean 143g **b** mean, takes all weights into account
3 a 71 kg **b** 70 kg **c** median, 53 kg is an extreme weight
4 a 59 **b** 54 **c** median, the higher average

Homework 13B

1 a mode = 16, median = 15, mean = 15.3 **b** mode = 5, median = 5, mean = 4.67 **2 a** 289 **b** 2 **c** 142 **d** 1.7

Homework 13C

1 a i 61–80 **ii** 58 **b i** 20.01–30.00 **ii** £27.40 **2 a** 79 **b** 35 minutes **c** mode **d** 94%

Homework 13D

1 a 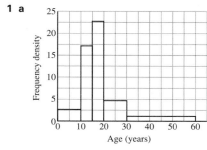 **b** 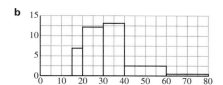 **c** Average age at the second show was higher.

2 a 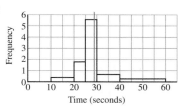 **b** 28.55 seconds **d** Area on both sides is same.

3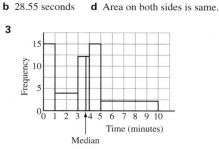

Homework 13E

2 d The frequency polygon as you can see how things have changed over the years.

Chapter 14

Homework 14A

1 $12t$ **2** $10y$ **3** $8y$ **4** $9w$ **5** $4t^2$ **6** $6b^2$ **7** $3w^2$ **8** $12y^2$ **9** $5p^2$ **10** $128t^2$ **11** $20m^2$ **12** $24t^2$ **13** $7mt$
14 $5yw$ **15** $8qt$ **16** $69nt$ **17** $30q$ **18** $10f$ **19** $18k$ **20** $35r$ **21** t^3 **22** p^3 **23** $5m^3$ **24** $3t^3$ **25** $8n^3$
26 $20r^3$ **27** t^4 **28** k^5 **29** $16n^5$ **30** $12t^7$ **31** $14a^7$ **32** $3k^7$ **33** k^3 **34** $10y^2$ **35** $18d^3$ **36** $-12p^6$
37 $5mq^2$ **38** $12m^2y$ **39** $12m^2t$ **40** $10q^2p^2$

Homework 14B

1 $12 + 3m$ **2** $18 + 6p$ **3** $16 - 4y$ **4** $18 + 21k$ **5** $12 - 20f$ **6** $8 - 46w$ **7** $7g + 7h$ **8** $8k + 16m$ **9** $12d - 6n$
10 $t^2 + 5t$ **11** $m^2 + 4m$ **12** $k^2 - 2k$ **13** $4g^2 + g$ **14** $3y^2 - 21y$ **15** $7p - 8p^2$ **16** $2m^2 + 10m$ **17** $3t^2 - 6t$

18 $15k - 3k^2$ **19** $8g^2 + 6g$ **20** $8h^2 - 12h$ **21** $12t - 10t^2$ **22** $12d^2 + 20de$ **23** $12y^2 + 5ky$ **24** $18m^3 - 6m^2p$
25 $y^3 + 7y$ **26** $h^4 + 9h$ **27** $k^3 - 4k$ **28** $3t^3 + 9t$ **29** $5h^4 - 10h$ **30** $4g^4 - 12g$ **31** $10m^3 + 5m^2$ **32** $8d^3 - 2d^4$
33 $12w^3 + 4wt$ **34** $15a^3 - 3ab$ **35** $14p^4 - 16mp$ **36** $3m^2 + 5m^3$ **37** $4t^4$ **38** $4g^2t - 3g^4$ **39** $14t^3 + 2mt^2$
40 $12h^3 + 15gh^2$

■ Homework 14C

1 a $9t$ **b** $7m$ **c** $7y$ **d** $10d$ **e** $2e$ **f** $3g$ **g** $2p$ **h** $4t$ **i** $5t^2$ **j** $3y^2$ **k** $7ab$ **l** a^2d
2 a $18 + 7t$ **b** $22 + 24k$ **c** $13 + 32m$ **d** $17 + 13y$ **e** $28 + 12f$ **f** $20 + 33g$
3 a $2 + 2h$ **b** $9g + 5$ **c** $6y + 11$ **d** $7t - 4$ **e** $17k + 16$ **f** $6e + 20$
4 a $5m + 2p + 2mp$ **b** $4k + 5h + 3hk$ **c** $t + 3n + 7nt$ **d** $p + 5q + 8pq$ **e** $6h + 12j + 11hj$ **f** $15y + 2t + 20ty$
5 a $4t^2 + 13t$ **b** $15y^2 + 7y$ **c** $11w^2 + 22w$ **d** $17p^2 + 6p$ **e** $m^2 + 8m$ **f** $14d - 3d^2$
6 a $2a^3 + 10a^2 + 15ab + 3ac$ **b** $4y^3 + 3y^2 + 12yw - 4ty$

■ Homework 14D

1 $3(3m + 4t)$ **2** $3(3t + 2p)$ **3** $4(m + 3k)$ **4** $2(2r + 3t)$ **5** $m(2n + 3)$ **6** $g(4g + 3)$ **7** $4(w - 2t)$ **8** $2(5p - 3k)$
9 $2(6h - 5k)$ **10** $2m(2p + k)$ **11** $2b(2c + 3k)$ **12** $4a(2b + c)$ **13** $y(3y + 4)$ **14** $t(5t - 3)$ **15** $d(3d - 2)$
16 $3m(2m - p)$ **17** $3p(p + 3t)$ **18** $4p(2t + 3m)$ **19** $2b(4a - 3c)$ **20** $4a(a - 2b)$ **21** $2t(4m - 3p)$ **22** $4at(5t + 3)$
23 $2bc(2b - 5)$ **24** $2b(2ac + 3ed)$ **25** $2(3a^2 + 2a + 5)$ **26** $3b(4a + 2c + 3d)$ **27** $t(6t + 3 + a)$ **28** $3mt(32t - 1 + 23m)$
29 $2ab(3b + 1 - 2a)$ **30** $5pt(t + 3 + p)$ **31** DNF **32** $m(3 + 2p)$ **33** $t(t - 5)$ **34** DNF **35** $2m(4m - 3p)$
36 DNF **37** $a(3a - 7b)$ **38** DNF **39** $b(7a - 4bc)$ **40** DNF **41** $3mt(2m + 3t)$ **42** DNF

■ Homework 14E

1 $x^2 + 7x + 10$ **2** $t^2 + 5t + 6$ **3** $w^2 + 5w + 4$ **4** $m^2 + 8m + 12$ **5** $k^2 + 6k + 8$ **6** $a^2 + 4a + 3$ **7** $x^2 + 2x - 3$
8 $t^2 + 2t - 24$ **9** $w^2 - w - 6$ **10** $f^2 - 3f - 4$ **11** $g^2 - 3g - 10$ **12** $y^2 + 3y - 10$ **13** $x^2 - x - 12$ **14** $p^2 - p - 6$
15 $k^2 - 4k - 5$ **16** $y^2 + 3y - 18$ **17** $a^2 + 2a - 8$ **18** $t^2 + t - 20$ **19** $x^2 - 5x + 6$ **20** $r^2 - 5r + 4$ **21** $m^2 - 8m + 7$
22 $g^2 - 8g + 15$ **23** $h^2 - 8h + 12$ **24** $n^2 - 10n + 16$ **25** $x^2 + 7x + 12$ **26** $20 - t - t^2$ **27** $12 - 4b - b^2$
28 $35 - 12y + y^2$ **29** $p^2 + p - 6$ **30** $8k - 15 - k^2$

■ Homework 14F

1 $12x^2 + 22x + 8$ **2** $6y^2 + 7y + 2$ **3** $12t^2 + 30t + 12$ **4** $6t^2 + t - 2$ **5** $18m^2 - 9m - 2$ **6** $20k^2 - 3k - 9$ **7** $12p^2 + p - 20$
8 $18w^2 + 27w + 4$ **9** $15a^2 - 17a - 4$ **10** $15r^2 - 11r + 2$ **11** $12g^2 - 11g + 2$ **12** $12d^2 - 5d - 2$ **13** $15 + 32p + 16p^2$
14 $15 + 19t + 6t^2$ **15** $2 + 11p + 15p^2$ **16** $21 - 2t - 8t^2$ **17** $20 + 3n - 2n^2$ **18** $20f^2 + 11f - 3$ **19** $10 - 7q - 12q^2$
20 $6 + 7p - 3p^2$ **21** $5 + 17t - 12t^2$ **22** $15 - 32t + 16t^2$ **23** $4 - 21x + 5x^2$ **24** $25m - 6 - 14m^2$ **25** $3x^2 + 8xy + 5y^2$
26 $12y^2 - 13yt - 4t^2$ **27** $25x^2 - 10xy - 3y^2$ **28** $x^2 - 5xy + 6y^2$ **29** $4m^2 + 17mp - 15p^2$ **30** $3t^2 - 13kt + 4k^2$ **31** $x^2 - 1$
32 $t^2 - 4$ **33** $y^2 - 9$ **34** $4m^2 - 9$ **35** $16k^2 - 9$ **36** $25h^2 - 1$ **37** $9 - 4x^2$ **38** $49 - 4t^2$ **39** $16 - 25y^2$ **40** $a^2 - b^2$
41 $9t^2 - k^2$ **42** $m^2 - 9p^2$ **43** $64k^2 - g^2$ **44** $a^2c^2 - b^2d^2$ **45** $x^4 - y^4$

■ Homework 14G

1 $x^2 + 8x + 16$ **2** $m^2 + 6m + 9$ **3** $25 + 10t + t^2$ **4** $4 + 4p + p^2$ **5** $m2 - 4m + 4$ **6** $t^2 - 8t + 16$ **7** $9 - 6m + m^2$
8 $36 - 12k + k^2$ **9** $4x^2 + 4x + 1$ **10** $9t^2 + 12t + 4$ **11** $1 + 8y + 16y^2$ **12** $4 + 4m + m^2$ **13** $9t^2 - 12t + 4$
14 $4x^2 - 4x + 1$ **15** $1 - 8t + 16t^2$ **16** $25 - 40r + 16r^2$ **17** $a^2 + 2ab + b^2$ **18** $x^2 - 2xy + y^2$ **19** $9t^2 + 6ty + y^2$
20 $m^2 - 4mn + 4n^2$ **21** $x^2 + 6x + 5$ **22** $x^2 - 8x - 9$ **23** $x^2 + 10x - 11$ **24** $x^2 - 2x$

■ Homework 14H

1 $(x + 1)(x + 6)$ **2** $(t + 2)(t + 2)$ **3** $(m + 1)(m + 10)$ **4** $(k + 3)(k + 8)$ **5** $(p + 6)(p + 4)$ **6** $(r + 2)(r + 9)$
7 $(w + 3)(w + 6)$ **8** $(x + 2)(x + 6)$ **9** $(a + 12)(a + 1)$ **10** $(k - 3)(k - 7)$ **11** $(f - 1)(f - 21)$ **12** $(b + 32)(b + 3)$
13 $(t + 3)(t + 2)$ **14** $(m - 4)(m - 1)$ **15** $(p - 2)(p - 5)$ **16** $(x - 4)(x - 9)$ **17** $(c - 4)(c - 8)$ **18** $(t - 3)(t - 12)$
19 $(y - 6)(y - 8)$ **20** $(j - 3)(j - 16)$ **21** $(p + 3)(p + 5)$ **22** $(y + 3)(y - 2)$ **23** $(t + 8)(t - 1)$ **24** $(x + 10)(x - 1)$
25 $(m - 4)(m + 3)$ **26** $(r + 7)(r - 1)$ **27** $(n - 9)(n + 2)$ **28** $(m - 22)(m + 2)$ **29** $(w - 8)(w + 3)$ **30** $(t + 10)(t - 9)$
31 $(x - 9)(x + 8)$ **32** $(t - 21)(t + 3)$ **33** $(d - 1)(d - 1)$ **34** $(y + 4)(y + 25)$ **35** $(t - 2)(t - 8)$ **36** $(m - 3)(m - 27)$
37 $(x - 6)(x - 24)$ **38** $(d - 6)(d + 2)$ **39** $(t + 5)(t - 4)$ **40** $(q + 8)(q - 7)$ **41** $(p - 2)(p + 1)$ **42** $(v - 7)(v + 5)$
43 $(t - 3)(t - 1)$ **44** $(m + 4)(m - 1)$ **45** $(x + 2)(x - 2)$ **46** $(t + 4)(t - 4)$ **47** $(m + 1)(m - 1)$ **48** $(2 + x)(2 - x)$
49 $(5 - t)(5 + t)$ **50** $(k - 7)(k + 7)$ **51** $(3 - y)(3 + y)$ **52** $(x - 5)(x + 5)$ **53** $(t - 8)(t + 8)$ **54** $(x + y)(x - y)$
55 $(x + 3y)(x - 3y)$ **56** $(x + 5y)(x - 5y)$

■ Homework 14 I

1 $x = -3, -2$ **2** $t = -4, -1$ **3** $a = -5, -3$ **4** $x = -4, 1$ **5** $x = -2, 5$ **6** $t = -3, 4$ **7** $x = 2, -1$ **8** $x = 1, -4$
9 $a = 6, -5$ **10** $x = 2, 5$ **11** $x = 2, 1$ **12** $a = 2, 6$ **13** $(x + 5)(x + 1) = 0, x = -1, -5$ **14** $(x + 3)(x + 6) = 0, x = -3, -6$
15 $(x - 8)(x + 1) = 0, x = 8, -1$ **16** $(x - 7)(x + 3) = 0, x = 7, -3$ **17** $(x + 5)(x - 2) = 0, x = -5, 2$
18 $(x + 5)(x - 3) = 0, x = -5, 3$ **19** $(t - 6)(t + 2) = 0, t = 6, -2$ **20** $(t - 6)(t + 3) = 0, t = 6, -3$ **21** $(x + 2)(x - 1) = 0, x = -2, 1$
22 $(x - 2)(x - 2) = 0, x = 2$ **23** $(m - 5)(m - 5) = 0, m = 5$ **24** $(t - 8)(t - 2) = 0, t = 8, 2$ **25** $(t + 3)(t + 4) = 0, t = -3, -4$
26 $(k - 6)(k + 3) = 0, k = 6, -3$ **27** $(a - 4)(a - 16) = 0, a = 4, 16$

■ Homework 14J

1 i $c = y - mx$ **ii** $x = \dfrac{y - c}{m}$ **2 i** $u = v + 10t$ **ii** $t = \dfrac{u - v}{10}$ **3 i** $x = \dfrac{T - 3y}{2}$ **ii** $y = \dfrac{T - 2x}{3}$ **4** $q = \sqrt{p}$

5 $q = \sqrt{(p + 3)}$ **6** $b = \sqrt{(a - c)}$ **7 a** 61.2 m/s **b** $t = \dfrac{v - u}{g}$ **c** 8.4 secs

Chapter 15

Homework 15A

1 a i £60 **ii** £80 **iii** £120 **b i** 50 **ii** 40 **iii** 25
2 a i £300 **ii** £200 **iii** £175 **b i** 400 **ii** 200 **iii** 150
3 a line graph passing through (250, 33), (500, 51) and (750, 69) **b** about £45

Homework 15B

1 a i 10.30 **ii** 11.10 **iii** 12.00 **b i** 50 km/h **ii** 75 km/h **iii** 50 km/h
2 a 20 km **b** 40 km **c** 60 km/h **d** 100 km/h
3

Homework 15C

1 a 2 **b** $\frac{1}{5}$ **c** −2 **d** $\frac{3}{2}$ **e** $\frac{1}{2}$ **f** $-\frac{3}{2}$ **g** 0 **h** $-\frac{4}{5}$ **i** $\frac{5}{2}$ **j** $-\frac{2}{5}$ **2 a** 17.5 kph **b** 30 mph
3 a 28.125 grams per ounce **b** 28.125 g

Homework 15D

1 a £4 **b** 0.059 **c** C = 0.059x units + 4 **2 a** £10 **b** 0.02 **c** C = 0.02x units + 10
3 a £25 **b** 0.047 **c** C = 0.047x units + 25

Chapter 16

Homework 16A

1 $x \times 3.5$, $y \times 3$; 2.5 **2 a** two sides in same ratio, included angle same. **b** 2 : 3 **c** Q **d** CA **3 a** 4.8 **b** 4.88

Homework 16B

1 a 9.6 **b** $1\frac{8}{9}$ **2 a** x = 6.875, y = 3.375 **b** x = 12, y = 12.5 **3** 3.69 m **4** 7.2 metres

Homework 16C

1 $\frac{4}{3}$ **2** $\frac{5}{3}$ **3** 6 **4** 20 **5** x = 5, y = 7 **6** x = 11.25, y = 6 **7** x = 20, y = 20.4 **8** x = 5, y = 7

Chapter 17

Homework 17A

1 a 65 cm **b** 145 cm **c** 117 cm **2 a** 51 cm **b** 44 cm **c** 80 cm **3 a** 74 cm **b** 48 cm **c** 89 cm

Homework 17B

1 5 cm **2** 4.41 cm **3** 10.6 cm **4** 35.4 cm **5** 20 cm **6** 19.2 cm **7 a** 40.15 m **b** 2100 m³

Homework 17C

1 a 23.7 cm **b** 22.2 cm **c** 6.9 cm **d** 32.6 cm **e** 8.1 cm **f** 760 m **g** 0.87 cm **h** 12 m
2 a 10 m **b** 27.2 cm **c** 29.4 m **d** 12.4 cm **3** 6.7 m

Homework 17D

1 10 cm **2** 39 cm **3** 78 cm **4** 7 cm **5** 17 cm **6** 50 cm **7** 35 cm **8** 72 cm **9** 24 cm **10** 40 cm **11** 30 cm
12 108 cm

Homework 17E

1 9 m   **2** 3.23 m   **3** 14.14 m   **4** 10 km   **5** 3.22 km   **6 a** 7.9 m   **b** 3.9 m   **7** $\sqrt{2}$ **8** 12 cm^2
9 Yes $61^2 = 60^2 + 11^2$ **10** 14.76 units   **11 a** 1 cm represents 2.5 km   **b** 40.4 km

Homework 17F

1 32.8 cm^2 9.16 cm^2 **2** 36.7 cm^2 **3** 43.3 cm^2 **4 a** 173.2 cm   **b** Only lengths have doubled. Area has quadrupled.
5 b 8, 8, 6 has area 22.25 cm^2 and 6, 6, 8 has 17.9 cm^2 **6** 54.5 mm^2

Chapter 18

Homework 18A

1 a 0.788   **b** 0.719   **c** 0.972   **d** 1   **2 a** 0.616   **b** 0.695   **c** 0.237   **d** 0   **3 a** 1   **b** 1   **c** 1   **d** 1   **e** All 1
4 a 1.280   **b** 1.036   **c** 4.102   **5 a** 1.280   **b** 1.036   **c** 4.102   **e** same
6 a 4.915   **b** 4.950   **c** 11.967   **d** 15.626   **7 a** 7.325   **b** 9.899   **c** 14.123   **d** 25.60   **8** $\sin x = \frac{5}{13}$, $\cos x = \frac{12}{13}$,
9 $\frac{3}{\sqrt{34}}$

Homework 18B

1 a 23.6°   **b** 45.0°   **c** 61.5°   **d** 41.8°   **2 a** 66.4°   **b** 45.0°   **c** 28.5°   **d** 70.5°
3 a 22°   **b** 19.5°   **c** 17.5°   **d** 38.7°   **4 a** 68°   **b** 70.5°   **c** 72.5°   **d** 51.3   **5** 36°

Homework 18D

1 a 0.899   **b** 0.956   **c** 1.50   **d** 0.982   **e** 0.899   **f** 1.15   **g** 0.602   **h** 0.970   **i** 1.04   **j** 0.990
2 a 13.9   **b** 6.17   **c** 5.37   **d** 76.3   **e** 2.27   **f** 0.939   **g** 4.82   **h** 2.87   **i** 2.70   **j** 4.02
3 a 8.64   **b** 12.8   **c** 57.5   **d** 1.06   **e** 4.67
4 a 1.04   **b** 0.946   **c** 0.454   **d** 19.1   **e** 0.469   **f** 0.559   **g** 3.27   **h** 0.755   **i** 0.875   **j** 0.532
5 a 5.36   **b** 2.14   **c** 37.7   **d** 39.0   **e** 4.08   **f** 3.15   **g** 15.4   **h** 7.46   **i** 1.56   **j** 6.39
6 a 1.11   **b** 7.40   **c** 6.86   **d** 3.49   **e** 5.06

Homework 18E

1 a 15.7   **b** 21.3°   **c** 80.9°   **d** 18.6°   **e** 30°   **f** 97.1   **2 a** 3.5   **b** 40   **c** 17.5   **3 a** 11.5 km   **b** 230°

Homework 18F

1 a 67.4°   **b** 11.3   **c** 42.8°   **d** 20.5°   **e** 72.1   **f** 54.1°   **2 a** 14   **b** 45   **c** 3.5   **3 a** 6.71 km   **b** 48.2°

Homework 18G

1 a 15.3   **b** 4.6   **c** 53.4°   **d** 7.64   **e** 29.1°   **f** 29.9   **2 a** 6   **b** 30   **c** $\frac{10}{3}$ **3** 81.5°

Homework 18H

1 a 65.0°   **b** 14.9   **c** 153.3   **d** 26.7°   **e** 327   **f** 49.3°   **g** 48.2°   **h** 230   **i** 45.8   **2** 6 cm   **3 a** 9.4 m   **b** 65.9°

Homework 18 I

1 70.3°   **2** 2.74 m to 1.39 m   **3** 54 m   **4** 5.04 m   **5** 29°   **6 a** 58.2°   **b** 7.75 m

Homework 18J

1 13.5 km   **2** 115 m   **3** 8.5 m   **4** 29.5°   **5** 31°   **6** 0.4°   **7 a** 64 m   **b** 9.1°

Homework 18K

1 a 78.2 km   **b** 33.2 km   **2 a** 10.3°   **b** 190.3°   **3** 128.7°   **4** 3.94 km
5 a 67.8 km   **b** 15.9 km   **c** 17.0 km   **d** 168.6°   **6 a ii** 226°   **b** 170 km   **c i** 28.1°   **ii** 344.1°

Homework 18L

1 9.59 cm   **2** 20.4°   **3** 17.4 m   **4 a** 30.1 cm^2 **b** 137.2 cm^2 **5** 63.6 cm^2 59.7 cm^2

Chapter 19

Homework 19A

1 centimetres   **2** kilometres (or metres)   **3** millimetres   **4** kilograms   **5** litres   **6** grams   **7** metres   **8** grams

Homework 19B

1 1.55 m **2** 9.5 cm **3** 0.78 m **4** 3.1 km **5** 3.1 m **6** 3.05 m **7** 15.6 cm **8** 2.18 km **9** 1.07 m **10** 13.24 m
11 0.175 km **12** 0.083 m **13** 62 cm **14** 21.3 **15** 5.12 **16** 8.15 **17** 2.3*t* **18** 3.2 c*l* **19** 1.36 *l* **20** 5.8 *l*
21 0.95*t* **22** 0.12 kg **23** 0.15 *l* **24** 3.5 *l* **25** 54 c*l* **26** 2.06*t* **27** 7.5 *l* **28** 3.8 kg **29** 6.05 *l* **30** 0.015 *l*
31 6.3 m³ **32** 45 cm³ **33** 2.35 m³ **34** 0.72 m³ **35** 820 cm **36** 71 000 m **37** 8600 mm **38** 156 mm **39** 83 cm
40 5150 m **41** 18.5 **42** 275 cm

Homework 19C

1 60 inches **2** 15 feet **3** 5280 yards **4** 96 ounces **5** 70 pounds **6** 4480 pounds **7** 32 pints **8** 84 inches
9 72 inches **10** 33 feet **11** 80 ounces **12** 6 feet **13** 84 pounds **14** 13 yards **15** 448 ounces **16** 2.5 miles
17 96 pints **18** 10 560 feet **19** 7 feet **20** 7.5 stones **21** 6 gallons **22** 3 pounds **23** 7 yards **24** 10 tonnes
25 126 720 inches **26** 16 pounds **27** 10 gallons **28** 20 stones **29** 6 miles **30** 71 680 ounces

Homework 19D

1 22.5 cm **2** 17.6 lbs **3** 64.4 km **4** 58.5 litres **5** 8550 ml **6** 12.2 gallons **7** 10″ **8** 37.27 miles **9** 14.55 kg
10 3.16 pints **11** 241.5 km **12** 200 cm **13** 140.8 lbs **14** 135 litres **15** 6840 ml **16** 74.53 miles **17** 68.18 kg
18 20″ **19** 13.66 miles **20** 26⅔ gallons **21** 13 500 ml **22** 4.39 pints **23** 30 cm **24** 6.4 kg **25** 3⅓ gallons
26 2200 lbs **27** 90 cm **28** 1 120 000″ **29** 1018.18 kg **30** 1.8 m

Homework 19E

1 $90.72 **2** DM 301.59 **3** €284.6 **4** BFr 18661.05 **5** SKr 2221.66 **6** ¥63760.2 **7** SFr 1701.05 **8** L 4 312 555
9 £55.51 **10** £145.20 **11** £6.80 **12** £2.56 **13** £12.66 **14** L 281 974.75 **15** £161.63 **16** £30.25
17 $272.16 **18** £240.73 **19** BFr 40 086.7 **20** £602.89 **21** £187.17 **22** £0.21 **23** SKr 1190.18 **24** £76.60
25 SFr 2093.6 **26** DM 1108.13 **27** £275.12 **28** €526.51 **29** $27.07 **30** $31.62 **31** $8.10 **32** $3.06
33 €527.04 **34** €3.95 **35** €314.24 **36** $0.29 **37** DM 28.12 **38** DM 60.61 **39** DM 14.65 **40** DM 640.24
41 FF 16.78 **42** FF 325.76 **43** FF 3048.88 **44** FF 1521.27

Homework 19F

1 a Large tin, because it costs 5.17p per g, while small tin costs 5.6p per g **b** 500 g tin because it costs 0.098p per g, while 250 g tin costs 0.125p per g **c** 650 g bag because it costs 0.095p per g, while 1 kg bag costs 0.096p per g **d** 220 ml bottle because it costs 0.86p per ml, while 85 ml tube costs 1.04p per ml **e** 800 g box because it costs 0.225p per g, while 550 g box costs 0.227p per g **f** both packs cost 0.377p per g to 3sf **g** 240 ml tub because it costs 0.3p per ml, while the 100 ml tub costs 0.38p per ml
2 a Large Bottle (0.84375 p per ml) **b** Buy 2 large bottles for £13.50 for 1600ml, which gives you 0.84375p per ml.

Chapter 20

Homework 20A

1

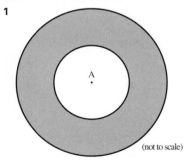

(not to scale)

2 a   **b**

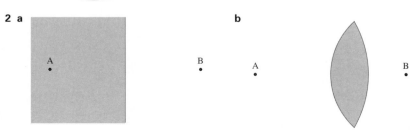

3 Sphere radius 1 metre

4 a 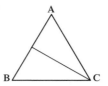 **b**  **c** 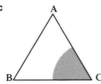 **d**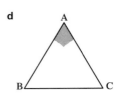

5   **6** 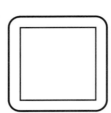 **7**

A •   B •

▬ Homework 20B

1 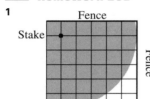 **2** 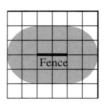 **3**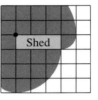

4 b No   **c** No   **5** No   **6 b** No

▬ Homework 20C

1 a 23°   **b** 84°   **c** 200°   **d** 54°   **e** 62°   **f** 60°   **2 a** 19°   **b** 27°   **c** 49°   **3 a** 78°   **b** 29°   **c** 78°
4 a $x = 20°, y = 105°$ **b** $x = 10°, y = 36°$ **6 a** 89°   **b** 46°

▬ Homework 20D

1 a $a = 68°, b = 100°$ **b** $d = 98°, e = 98°, f = 82°$ **c** $d = 95°, e = 111°$ **d** $n = 142°, m = 118°$
2 a 89°   **b** 98°   **c** $x = 82°, y = 33°$ **3 a** $x = 52°, y = 104°$ **b** $x = 120°, y = 120°$ **c** $x = 95°, y = 75°$
4 BAC = 180 – ACD (co-interior), ABD = 180 – ACD (opposite in cyclic quad), Hence BAC = ABD

▬ Homework 20E

1 a 48°   **b** 30°   **2 a** 4 cm   **b** 9.2 cm   **3 a** $x = 16°, y = 74°$ **b** $x = 80°, y = 50°$ **4 a** 18°   **b** 16°
5 a 42°   **b** 138°

Chapter 21

▬ Homework 21A

1

x	0	1	2	3	4
y	1	2	3	4	5

2

x	0	1	2	3	4
y	1	3	5	7	9

3

x	0	1	2	3	4
y	1	4	7	10	13

4

x	0	1	2	3	4
y	–1	0	1	2	3

5 a graphs of $y = x – 2$ and $y = 2x – 1$ **b** $(–1, –3)$ **6 a** graphs of $y = 2x$ and $y = x + 2$ **b** $(2, 4)$

▬ Homework 21B

1 end points at $(0, 3)$ and $(5, 13)$ **2** end points at $(0, –1)$ and $(5, 14)$ **3** end points at $(0, –2)$ and $(12, 4)$
4 end points at $(–2, –3)$ and $(2, 5)$ **5** end points at $(–6, 2)$ and $(6, 8)$

6 a end points at (0, −1) and (5, 14), (0, 3) and (5, 13)   **b** (4, 11)
7 a end points at (0, −3) and (6, 21), (0, 2) and (6, 20)   **b** (5, 17)
8 a end points at (0, 1) and (12, 7), (0, 2) and (12, 6)   **b** (6, 4)
9 a end points at (0, 3) and (4, 11), (0, −1) and (4, 7)   **b** no, the lines are parallel
10 a

x	0	1	2	3	4	5	6
y	6	5	4	3	2	1	0

b graph of $x + y = 3$

▰▰ Homework 21C

1 a 2   **b** −3   **c** $\frac{2}{3}$ **d** $-\frac{1}{3}$ **e** 4   **f** $-\frac{4}{5}$ **g** $-\frac{1}{4}$ **h** $\frac{1}{6}$ **i** 7   **j** −4

▰▰ Homework 21D

2 b (−3, −7)   **3 b** $(\frac{1}{2}, -2\frac{1}{2})$

▰▰ Homework 21E

1 a $y = x + 2$ **b** $y = 3x − 1$ **c** $5y = 2x + 4$
2 a i $y = x, y = −x$ **ii** reflection in x- and y-axes   **b i** $y = \frac{1}{2}x + 2, y = -\frac{1}{2}x + 2$ **ii** reflection in y-axis and $y = 2$
   c i $2y = 5x + 3, 2y = −5x + 13$ **ii** reflection in $x = 1$ and $y = 4$
3 $y = 2x + 4, y = 2x − 6, y = -\frac{1}{2}x + 4, y = -\frac{1}{2}x + \frac{3}{2}$

▰▰ Homework 21F

2 a

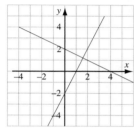

b $x = 1.6, y = 1.2$ **3 a**

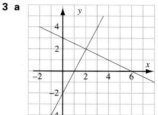

b $x = 2, y = 2$

▰▰ Homework 21G

1 (5, −1)   **2** (3, 7)   **3** (−1, 3)   **4** Parallel   **5** (4, −2)   **6** (1.5, 6.5)   **7** (−3, 8)   **8** (−1, 5)   **9** (−3, 3)   **10** (−2, 4)
11 (2.5, 3.5)   **12** (3.5, −1.5)

Chapter 22

▰▰ Homework 22A

1 a

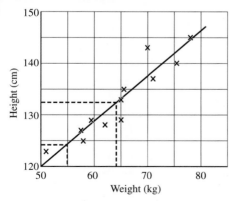

Height (cm) vs Weight (kg)

c 64 kg   **d** 124 cm

2 a

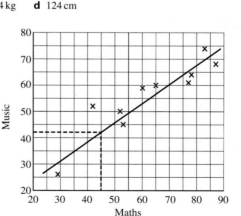

Music vs Maths

c Irene
d 42
e 95

Homework 22B

1

1997	1998	1999	2000
	83	90	98.25
	84.25	91	98.75
	81.75	97.75	101.75
84	88	97	102.75

The trend shows a general increase.

2

	Monday	Tuesday	Wednesday	Thursday	Friday	Saturday	Sunday
1st week							32.3
2nd week	30.8	27.7	26.8	24.5	21.5	24.6	26.8
3rd week	25.8	23.5	23.2	23.1	21.2	23.1	25.8
4th week	24.9	23.6	23.3	22.2	19.7	21.8	24.4

The trend starts well, but then settles down to an average of about 23

3

	Jan	Feb	Mar	Apr	May	June	July	Aug	Sep	Oct	Nov	Dec
1999			25.0	26.3	26.3	20.7	21.7	20.7	27.7	26.0	27.3	26.0
2000	26.3	26.3	26.3	26.7	26.0	27.3	27.0	27.3	27.3	29.7	28.3	27.3

The sales start increasing, but take a dip in mid summer, to start rising slightly showing a good increase towards the end of 2000.

Homework 22C

1 a

Time (seconds)	Number of runners	
$200 < x \le 240$	3	3
$240 < x \le 260$	7	10
$260 < x \le 280$	12	22
$280 < x \le 300$	23	45
$300 < x \le 320$	7	52
$320 < x \le 340$	5	57
$340 < x \le 360$	5	62

b

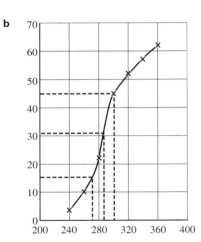

c Median = 283, IQR = 30

2 a

Number of visits	Number of pages	
$0 < x \le 50$	6	6
$50 < x \le 100$	9	15
$100 < x \le 150$	15	30
$150 < x \le 200$	25	55
$200 < x \le 250$	31	86
$250 < x \le 300$	37	123
$300 < x \le 350$	32	155
$350 < x \le 400$	17	172
$400 < x \le 450$	5	177

b

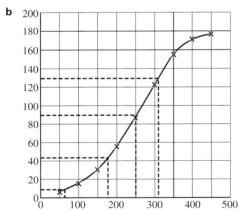

c Median = 250, IQR = 135   **d** 7 pages

1 a

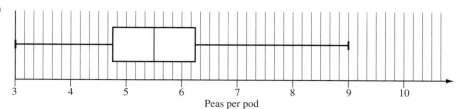

b Distributions similar is shape but the older gardener has about 2.2 peas more per pod.

2 a

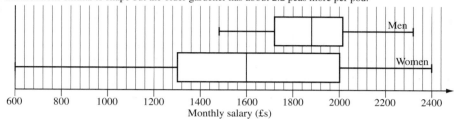

b Men's distribution is very compact. Women's is more spread out and women generally get paid less than men.
3 a The flying bug batteries have a slightly higher median but are very inconsistent. The Ever Steady are very consistent.
b Ever Steady because they are very reliable.
4 a

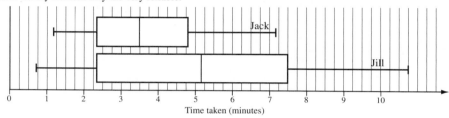

b Jack has lower median and a more consistent distribution.
c Jill because she takes too long on the phone.
5 a 57   **b**

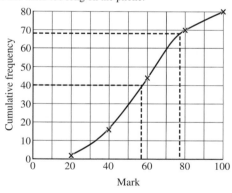

c i 58   **ii** 74
d Second school has about the same median but a much more compact and symmetrical distribution.

Chapter 23

Homework 23A

1 a $\frac{1}{5}, \frac{3}{20}, \frac{1}{5}, \frac{9}{50}, \frac{17}{100}, \frac{7}{40}, \frac{17}{100}$ **b** $\frac{1}{6}$ **2 a** $\frac{11}{60}, \frac{17}{120}, \frac{7}{40}, \frac{3}{20}, \frac{13}{60}, \frac{2}{15}$ **b** 20   **c** yes, all frequencies are close to 20
3 a i 90   **ii** 60   **iii** 30   **b** 0.4

Homework 23B

1 a $\frac{1}{6}$ **b** $\frac{1}{2}$ **c** $\frac{1}{13}$ **d** $\frac{1}{4}$ **e** $\frac{1}{3}$ **2 a** $\frac{1}{2}$ **b** $\frac{1}{3}$ **c** $\frac{1}{2}$ **d** $\frac{1}{52}$ **3 a** $\frac{1}{2}$ **b** $\frac{1}{3}$ **c** $\frac{5}{6}$ **4** $\frac{1}{160}$
5 a AB, AC, AD, AE, AF, BC, BD, BE, BF, CD, CE, CF, DE, DF, EF   **b** 1   **c** $\frac{1}{15}$ **d** 8   **e** $\frac{8}{15}$ **f** $\frac{2}{5}$
6 a $\frac{5}{12}$ **b i** 4   **ii** 7   **c i** $\frac{4}{11}$ **ii** $\frac{7}{11}$ **7 a** $\frac{1}{6}$ **b** $\frac{2}{3}$ **c** $\frac{5}{6}$ **d** 0   **e** 1
8 a $\frac{1}{3}$ **b** $\frac{1}{2}$ **c** $\frac{1}{4}$ **d** $\frac{1}{3}$ **e** $\frac{7}{12}$ **f** $\frac{3}{4}$ **9 a** $\frac{9}{40}$ **b** $\frac{3}{5}$

Homework 23C

1 a Yes **b** Yes **c** Yes **d** No **e** No **2** b

3 a i $\frac{4}{11}$ **ii** $\frac{2}{11}$ **iii** $\frac{4}{11}$ **b i** Yes **ii** No **iii** Yes **c** iii

4 a Ann, Joan,   Ann, Jack   Ann, John,   Ann, Arthur,   Ann, Ethel   Joan, Jack,   Joan, John,   Joan, Arthur,
Joan, Ethel,   Jack, John,   Jack, Arthur,   Jack, Ethel   John, Arthur,   John, Ethel   Arthur, Ethel

  b i $\frac{1}{5}$ **ii** $\frac{1}{5}$ **iii** $\frac{4}{15}$ **iv** $\frac{11}{15}$ **c** i ii iv **d** ii

5 $\frac{1}{6}$ **6 a** i, iv, v **b** i **7** May be windy and rainy. Windy and rainy are not independent events.

Homework 23D

1 100 **2** 250 **3 a** 52 **b** 8 **c** 4 **d** 2 **4** 21 **5** 1667 **6 a** 100 **b** 100 **c** 130 **d** 0 **7** 120

8 a You cannot add probabilities for events like this. **b** Increase as he is more experienced

9 a 28 000 **b** 90% of 112 is 100.8 out of 200 so they should win.

Homework 23E

1 a $\frac{1}{6}$ **b** $\frac{1}{6}$ **c** $\frac{2}{3}$ **2 a** $\frac{1}{2}$ **b** $\frac{1}{2}$ **c** 1 **3 a** $\frac{1}{13}$ **b** $\frac{1}{13}$ **c** $\frac{2}{13}$ **4 a** $\frac{3}{10}$ **b** $\frac{3}{10}$ **c** $\frac{3}{5}$

5 a $\frac{1}{3}$ **b** $\frac{2}{3}$ **c** $\frac{11}{15}$ **d** $\frac{11}{15}$ **e** $\frac{1}{3}$ **6 a** 0.75 **b** 0.6 **c** 0.25 **d** 0.6 **e i** because 2 and red overlap **ii** 0.5

7 a $\frac{3}{5}$ **b** $\frac{4}{5}$ **c** $\frac{2}{5}$ **8 a** 3 **b** not certain he has 3 double yolks to start with **9 a** $\frac{11}{15}$ **b** $\frac{2}{3}$ **c** 0 **d** $\frac{2}{3}$

Homework 23F

1 (See diagram on page 437 of main pupil book) **a i** $\frac{1}{6}$ **ii** $\frac{1}{4}$ **iii** $\frac{1}{6}$ **iv** $\frac{5}{36}$ **v** $\frac{1}{2}$ **vi** $\frac{29}{36}$

2 a $\frac{1}{6}$ **b** $\frac{11}{36}$ **c** $\frac{1}{9}$ **d** $\frac{3}{4}$ **e** $\frac{1}{36}$ **f** $\frac{11}{36}$ **g** $\frac{10}{36}$

3

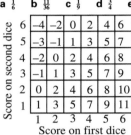

a $\frac{1}{12}$ **b** $\frac{1}{6}$ **c** $\frac{1}{2}$ **d** $\frac{1}{6}$ **e** $\frac{13}{36}$

4 a $\frac{1}{2}$ **b** $\frac{1}{2}$ **c** $\frac{3}{4}$ **5 a** $\frac{1}{4}$ **b** $\frac{3}{8}$ **c** $\frac{7}{8}$ **6 a** $\frac{1}{12}$ **b** $\frac{1}{4}$

7 a DD, TD, HD, TT, HH, TH

b

Hyac	DH	DH	TH	HH
Tulip	DT	DT	TT	HT
Daff	DD	DD	TD	HD
Daff	DD	DD	TD	HD
	Daff	**Daff**	**Tulip**	**Hyac**

c $\frac{1}{4}$

d more daffodils

Homework 23G

1

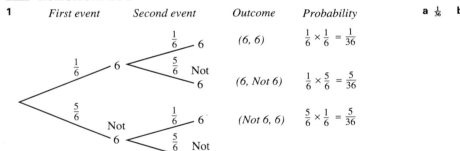

a $\frac{1}{36}$ **b** $\frac{10}{36}$ **c** $\frac{25}{36}$

2 a $\frac{3}{5}$ **b**

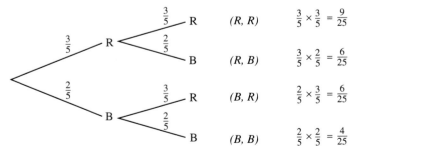

c i $\frac{9}{25}$ **ii** $\frac{12}{25}$ **iii** $\frac{21}{25}$

3

First event   Second event   Outcome   Probability   **a** $\frac{1}{4}$ **b** $\frac{3}{4}$ **c i** $\frac{1}{16}$ **ii** $\frac{7}{16}$

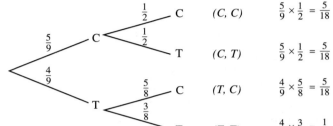

Outcome	Probability
(S, S)	$\frac{1}{4} \times \frac{1}{4} = \frac{1}{16}$
$(S, \text{Not } S)$	$\frac{1}{4} \times \frac{3}{4} = \frac{3}{16}$
$(\text{Not } S, S)$	$\frac{3}{4} \times \frac{1}{4} = \frac{3}{16}$
$(\text{Not } S, \text{Not } S)$	$\frac{3}{4} \times \frac{3}{4} = \frac{9}{16}$

4 a i $\frac{5}{9}$ **ii** $\frac{4}{9}$ **b i** 8   **ii** 4   **c i** 8   **ii** 3

d   First choice   Second choice   Outcome   Probability   **e i** $\frac{4}{9}$ **ii** $\frac{5}{6}$

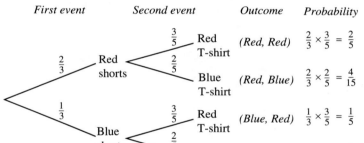

Outcome	Probability
(C, C)	$\frac{5}{9} \times \frac{1}{2} = \frac{5}{18}$
(C, T)	$\frac{5}{9} \times \frac{1}{2} = \frac{5}{18}$
(T, C)	$\frac{4}{9} \times \frac{5}{8} = \frac{5}{18}$
(T, T)	$\frac{4}{9} \times \frac{3}{8} = \frac{1}{6}$

5 0.2

6 a $\frac{1}{3}$ **b**

First event   Second event   Outcome   Probability   **c i** $\frac{8}{15}$ **ii** $\frac{7}{15}$ **iii** $\frac{13}{15}$

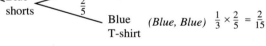

Outcome	Probability
(Red, Red)	$\frac{2}{3} \times \frac{3}{5} = \frac{2}{5}$
$(Red, Blue)$	$\frac{2}{3} \times \frac{2}{5} = \frac{4}{15}$
$(Blue, Red)$	$\frac{1}{3} \times \frac{3}{5} = \frac{1}{5}$
$(Blue, Blue)$	$\frac{1}{3} \times \frac{2}{5} = \frac{2}{15}$

7 a

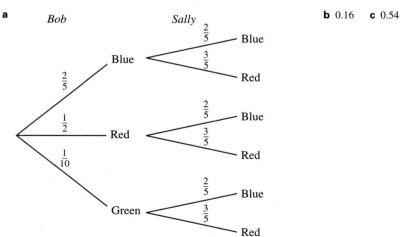

   b 0.16   **c** 0.54

■ Homework 23H

1 a $\frac{1}{16}$ **b** $\frac{3}{8}$ **2 a** $\frac{1}{16}$ **b** $\frac{1}{8}$ **3 a** $\frac{1}{17}$ **b** $\frac{13}{102}$ **4** $\frac{1}{54}$ **5 a** $\frac{9}{100}$ **b** $\frac{21}{50}$ **6 a** $\frac{1}{15}$ **b** $\frac{7}{15}$ **7 a** $\frac{1}{6}$ **b** $\frac{1}{36}$ **c** $\frac{13}{36}$

Chapter 24

Homework 24A

1 $7 \times 11 \times 13 \times 6 = 6006$, $7 \times 11 \times 13 \times 7 = 7007$　**2** $3 \times 7 \times 13 \times 37 \times 6 = 60606$, $3 \times 7 \times 13 \times 37 \times 7 = 70707$
3 $7 \times 9 = 8^2 - 1 = 63$, $8 \times 10 = 9^2 - 1 = 80$　**4** $7 \times 11 = 9^2 - 4 = 77$, $8 \times 12 = 10^2 - 1 = 96$　**5** 9009　**6** 80808　**7** 9999
8 9996　**9** 15015　**10** 151515　**11** 999996　**12** 999999

Homework 24B

1 a $12, 14, 16 : +2$　**b** $15, 18, 21 : +3$　**c** $32, 64, 128 : \times 2$　**d** $33, 40, 47 : +7$　**e** $30\,000, 300\,000, 3\,000\,000 : \times 10$
 f $25, 36, 49 :$ square numbers
2 a $34, 55 :$ add previous two terms　**b** $23, 30 :$ add one more each time
3 a $112, 224, 448 : \times 2$　**b** $38, 45, 52 : +7$　**c** $63, 127, 255 :$ add twice the difference each time
 d $30, 25, 19 :$ subtract one more each time　**e** $38, 51, 66 :$ add add two more each time　**f** $25, 32, 40 :$ add one more each time
 g $13, 15, 16 : +2, +1$　**h** $20, 23, 26 : +3$　**i** $32, 40, 49 :$ add one more each time　**j** $0, -5, -11 :$ subtract one more each time
 k $0.32, 0.064, 0.0128 : \div 5$　**l** $0.1875, 0.09375, 0.046875 : \div 2$

Homework 24C

1 a $4, 7, 10, 13, 16$　**b** $1, 3, 5, 7, 9$　**c** $6, 10, 14, 18, 22$　**d** $2, 8, 18, 32, 50$　**e** $0, 3, 8, 15, 24$
2 a $3, 4, 5, 6, 7$　**b** $3, 7, 11, 15, 19$　**c** $1, 5, 9, 13, 17$　**d** $2, 5, 10, 17, 26$　**e** $3, 9, 19, 33, 51$

3 a $\frac{3}{2}, \frac{5}{3}, \frac{7}{4}, \frac{9}{5}, \frac{11}{6}, \frac{13}{7}$　**b** 1.999　**c** 2　**4 a i** $\frac{11}{12}$　**ii** $\frac{n}{n+1}$　**b** $2, \frac{3}{2}, \frac{4}{3}, \frac{5}{4}$

Homework 24D

1 a $2n + 3$　**b** $4n - 1$　**c** $5n + 1$　**d** $6n - 3$　**e** $3n + 1$　**f** $7n - 4$
2 a 101　**b** 201　**c** 253　**d** 296　**e** 152　**f** 345
3 a i $3n + 1$　**ii** 301　**iii** 100　**b i** $2n + 5$　**ii** 205　**iii** 99, 101　**c i** $5n - 2$　**ii** 498　**iii** 98
 d i $4n - 3$　**ii** 397　**iii** 101　**e i** $8n - 6$　**ii** 794　**iii** 98　**f i** $n + 4$　**ii** 104　**iii** 100

Homework 24E

1 a

b $5n + 1$　**c** 126　**d** 39th
2 a
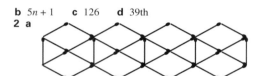
b $9n + 1$　**c** 541　**d** 11th

3
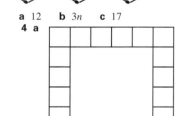
a 12　**b** $3n$　**c** 17
4 a
b $3n + 2$　**c** 152　**d** 99

5 a

b

Number of enclosures	1	2	3	4	5	6	7	8
Number of posts	6	9	12	15	18	21	24	27

c 63　**d** $3n + 3$

Homework 24F

1 a i $36, 49$　**ii** n^2　**b i** $37, 50$　**ii** $n^2 + 1$　**c i** $40, 53$　**ii** $n^2 + 4$　**d i** $72, 98$　**ii** $2n^2$　**e i** $56, 69$　**ii** $n^2 + 20$
2 a i $40, 54$　**ii** $n(n + 3)$　**b i** $63, 80$　**ii** $(n + 2)(n + 4)$　**c i** $30, 42$　**ii** $n(n + 1)$　**d i** $15, 21$　**ii** $\frac{1}{2}n(n + 1)$
 e i $42, 56$　**ii** $(n + 1)(n + 2)$
3 a i $n^2 + 2n + 5$　**ii** 2605　**b i** $3n + 5$　**ii** 155　**c i** $(n + 1)(n + 3)$　**ii** 2703　**d i** $(n - 1)(n + 3)$　**ii** 2597
4 a i 14　**b i** 57　**ii** add on 3 more each time

Chapter 25

Homework 25A

1 a

x	–3	–2	–1	0	1	2	3
$y = 2x^2$	18	8	2	0	2	8	18

b $y = 4$, **c** ±2.2

2 a

x	–5	–4	–3	–2	–1	0	1	2	3	4	5
$y = x^2 + 3$	28	19	12	7	4	3	4	7	12	19	28

b 9.2, **c** ±2.6

3 a

x	–3	–2	–1	0	1	2	3	4
$y = x^2 – 3x + 2$	20	12	6	2	0	0	2	6

b 8.75, **c** –0.15, 3.15

Homework 25B

1 a

x	–1	0	1	2	3	4	5
$y = x^2 – 3x + 2$	6	2	0	0	1	6	12

b 1, 2

2 a

x	–1	0	1	2	3	4	5	6
$y = x^2 – 5x + 4$	10	4	0	–2	–2	0	4	10

b 1, 4,

3 a

x	–5	–4	–3	–2	–1	0	1	2
$y = x^2 + 4x – 6$	–1	–6	–9	–10	–9	–6	–1	6

b 1.15, –5.15

Homework 25C

1 a

x	–12	–6	–4	–3	–2	–1	1	2	3	4	6	12
$y = \frac{12}{x}$	–1	–2	–3	–4	–6	–12	12	6	4	3	2	1

b i 8 **ii** 2.2 (approx)

2 a

x	–8	–5	–4	–2	–1	1	2	4	5	8
$y = \frac{8}{x}$	–1	–1.6	–2	–4	–8	8	4	2	1.6	1

b i 2.3 (approx) **ii** 1.6 (approx)

3 a

x	1	2	5	10	25	50
$y = \frac{50}{x}$	50	25	10	5	2	1

c 1.58 to 3sf

Homework 25D

1 a

x	–3	–2	–1	0	1	2	3
$y = x^3 + 1$	–26	–7	0	1	2	9	28

b 2.7

2 a

x	–2	–1	0	1	2	3
$y = x^3 + 2x$	–12	–3	0	3	12	33

b 20.6

3 b 2.6

Chapter 26

Homework 26A

1 $3a + b$ **2** $6x$ **3** $5p$ **4** $2r + 2\pi r$ **5** $2R + \pi R$ **6** $3q + 2p$ **7** $\pi(a + b)$

Homework 26B

1 $\frac{1}{2}bh$ **2** $2ab$ **3** $\frac{1}{2}\pi r^2 + \frac{1}{2}\pi R^2 + a(R + r)$ **4** $d^2 + \frac{\pi d^2}{2}$ **5** $bk + \frac{1}{2}h(a + b)$ **6** $x^2 – y^2$ **7** $\pi h(a + b)$

Homework 26C

1 x^3 **2** $2\pi r^3$ **3** $x(x^2 – y^2)$ **4** $a^2 b$ **5** $\pi(R^2 – r^2)h$ **6** $abc + a^2 c$ **7 a** Volume **b** Perimeter **c** Area

Homework 26D

1 a L **b** A **c** V **d** N **e** L **f** A **g** N **h** V **i** N **j** N
2 a A **b** V **c** V **d** V **e** A **f** V **g** L **h** V **3 a** represents a length **b ii** it is Length × length = area

Homework 26E

1 a C **b** I **c** I **d** I **e** I **f** C **g** I **h** C
2 a C, A **b** C, L **c** I, **d** C, L **e** C, V **f** I **g** C, A **h** C, N **3 a** 2 **b** 1 **c** 2 **d** 2
4 a V **b** V **c** L **d** L **e** None

Higher Mathematics for GCSE: Answers

Chapter 1

Homework 1A

1 a £84 **b** 14.84 kg **c** £43.26 **2 a** 374 g **b** 67.2 m **c** £49.20 **3** £35 568 **4** 15 336 **5** 907 **6** 52 girls
7 £45 864

Homework 1B

1 a £7.68 **b** 15.98 kg **c** 235.2 m **2 a** 324 g **b** 374 m **c** 270 cm **3** £7392 **4** 64 **5** 7
6 a 450 g **b** 550 g **7** 680 units

Homework 1C

1 a 5.5 cm **b** 6.05 cm **c** 7.32 cm **d** 9.74 cm **2 a** £32 413.50 **b** 7 years **3 a** £291.60 **b** £314.93 **c** £367.33
4 a 1725 **b** 1984 **c** 2624
5 After 11 years the sycamore is 93.26 cm tall and the conifer is 93.05 cm tall.
After 12 years the sycamore is 100.73 cm tall and the conifer is 107 cm tall.

Homework 1D

1 a 25% **b** 6% **c** 5% **d** 50% **e** 25% **f** 65% **2 a** 40% **b** 68% **3** 16%
4 Maths 84% English 70% Science 62.5% French 45% **5** 5% **6** 22%

Homework 1E

1 a 800 g **b** 96 m **c** 840 cm **2 a** 70 kg **b** £180 **c** 40 hours **3** Jumper £12 Socks £1.60 Trousers £20
4 £15 **5** £180 **6** £50 **7** 800 g **8** 550 CDs

Homework 1F

1 a 3.7 **b** 8.7 **c** 5.4 **d** 18.8 **e** 0.4 **f** 26.3 **g** 3.8 **h** 10.1 **i** 11.1 **j** 12.0
2 a 6.72 **b** 4.46 **c** 1.97 **d** 3.49 **e** 5.81 **f** 2.56 **g** 21.80 **h** 12.99 **i** 2.30 **j** 5.56
3 a 0.09 **b** 4.56 **c** 2.10 **d** 0.763 **e** 7.1 **f** 8.90 **g** 23.781 **h** 1.0
4 a 7 **b** 9 **c** 3 **d** 8 **e** 8 **f** 3 **g** 2 **h** 2 **i** 5 **j** 4

Homework 1G

1 a 50 000 **b** 60 000 **c** 30 000 **d** 90 000 **e** 90 000 **f** 50 **g** 90 **h** 30 **i** 100 **j** 200 **k** 0.5 **l** 0.3
  m 0.006 **n** 0.05 **o** 0.0009 **p** 10 **q** 90 **r** 90 **s** 200 **t** 1000
2 Hellaby 850 to 949 Hook 645 to 654 Hundleton 1045 to 1054
3 a 6700 **b** 36 000 **c** 69 000 **d** 42 000 **e** 27 000 **f** 7000 **g** 2200 **h** 960 **i** 440 **j** 330
4 a 50 000 **b** 6200 **c** 89.7 **d** 220 **e** 8 **f** 1.1 **g** 730 **h** 6000 **i** 67 **j** 6 **k** 8 **l** 9.75 **m** 26
  n 30 **o** 870 **p** 40 **q** 0.085 **r** 0.0099 **s** 0.08 **j** 0.0620

Homework 1H

1 a 28 000 **b** 42 000 **c** 210 **d** 20 000 **e** 2000 **f** 2100 **g** 5 **h** 9 **i** 700 **j** 75 **k** 50 **l** 8
2 a £4000 **b** £2000 **c** £1500 **3 a** £30 000 **b** £36 000 **4** 6 litres **5** £1400 **6** 20p
7 a 105 km **b** 450 km **b** 5000 km

Homework 1 I

1 a 1.62 m **b** 20 minutes **c** 3 kg **d** 1.24°C **e** 24 000 **2** 25 jars **3** 65 minutes to 2 sf
4 a £2630 to 3 sf **b** £604 to 3 sf **c** £86.30 to 3 sf **5** 62 mph **6** £217

Chapter 2

Homework 2A

1 a 9.4 cm **b** 31.4 cm **c** 50.3 m **d** 44.0 cm **e** 20.1 cm **f** 22.0 cm **2** 200π **3 a** 15.7 cm **b** 2 **4** 18.0 cm
5 $6\pi + 12$ **6** 1700 revs **7** 3.82 cm

Homework 2B

1 a $16\pi \text{ cm}^2$ **b** 153.9 cm^2 **c** 254.5 cm^2 **d** $\pi \text{ m}^2$ **e** 1385.4 cm^2 **f** 0.6 cm^2 **2** 66 m^2 **3** 88.4 cm^2 **4** 3.99 m
5 49.7 cm^2 **6** 329 m^2

Homework 2C

1 a 8.7 cm 43.6 cm² **b** 11 cm 38.5 cm² **2** 2.5π 6.25π **3 a** 51.4 cm **b** 80.5 cm **4 a** 134 cm² **b** 222.7 cm²
5 268 m²

Homework 2D

1 a 23.1 cm 28 cm² **b** 36 cm 66.5 cm² **2 a** 89 m² **b** 35.5 cm² **3 a** 45 cm² **b** 24 cm²
4 a is 10 cm² and **b** is 9.6 cm² **5** 64.7%

Homework 2E

1 0.9 g/cm³ **2** 62.5 g/cm³ **3** 30 g **4** 389 cm³ **5** 1350 g **6** 909 cm³ **7** 5.25 g/cm³ **8** 996 Tonnes **9** 1.11 g/cm³

Homework 2F

1 i 100π cm³ **ii** 40π cm² **2 i** 3400 cm³ **ii** 850 cm² **3 a i** 785 cm³ **ii** 471 cm² **b i** 393 cm³ **ii** 314 cm²
4 2 cm **5** 18 cm **6** 3 cm **7** 159 cm³ **8** 297 cm² **9** 125π cm³

Homework 2G

1 a 10.5 cm² 42 cm³ **b** 25 cm² 250 cm³ **2 i** 190 g **ii** 187.8 g **iii** 189 g

Homework 2H

1 a 70 cm³ **b** 2080 cm³ **2** 600 cm³ **3** 120 cm³ **4** 3 cm **5** 171.5 cm³

Homework 2 I

1 a i 8042 cm³ **ii** 2513 cm² **b i** 302 cm³ **ii** 302 cm² **2** 24π cm² **3** 96π cm³
4 a 62.8 cm **b** 10 cm **c** 12 cm **d** 120π cm² **e** 6.6 cm **f** 220π cm³ **5** 2.8 cm **6** 216°

Homework 2J

1 a 36π cm³ **b** 4500π cm³ **2 a** 64π cm² **b** 100π cm² **3** 14 000 cm³ 2800 cm² **4 a** 4.0 cm **b** 3.6 cm
5 4.6 cm **6** 752 cm³ **7 a** 264π cm³ **b** 120π cm²

Chapter 3

Homework 3A

1 a $3+x$ **b** $7k$ **c** $x-4$ **d** kt **e** $k+y$ **f** $\frac{x}{3}$ **g** $y-t$ **h** $\frac{5}{x}$ **i** h^2

2 a $4a$ **b** $5b$ **c** $7c$ **d** $7d$ **e** $11e$ **f** $10f$ **g** $-2v$ **h** $4x$ **i** 0
3 a $11y+7x$ **b** $m+6p$ **c** $7x+2$ **d** $3x+7$ **e** $6p+2t$ **f** $6x+4$
4 a $5f+10$ **b** $4k-4$ **c** $3t+6$ **d** $24d+16$ **e** $6t-15$ **f** $14m+35$ **g** $12+20w$ **h** $10-15x$
5 a $10x+15y$ **b** $30t+21p$ **c** $18t-27q$ **d** $16p+14t$ **e** $-5t-18n$ **f** $2p+32t$ **6** £$(P-T)$ **7** £$\frac{B}{4}$

Homework 3B

1 i 15 **ii** 27 **iii** 47 **2 i** 5 **ii** 14 **iii** 29 **3 i** 9 **ii** 12 **iii** 19 **4 i** 2 **ii** −4 **iii** −16
5 i 11 **ii** 47 **iii** 71 **6 i** 0.5 **ii** 6.5 **iii** 26.5 **7 i** −8 **ii** −3 **iii** 109.5 **8 i** −6 **ii** −3 **iii** 13.5
9 i 11 **ii** 3 **iii** 4.3 **10 i** −11 **ii** −15 **iii** 7 **11 i** 13 **ii** 16 **iii** 5.4 **12 i** 11 **ii** −14 **iii** −0.75
13 i 8.5 **ii** −4.7 **iii** 4.24 **14 i** 3.5 **ii** 19.4 **iii** 8.03

Homework 3C

1 a 16 **b** 16 **c** 1.21 **2 a** 25 **b** 169 **3 a** 16 **b** 21 **4 a** 51 **b** 36 **c** 19 **5 a** 17 **b** 28
6 a −14 **b** 25 **c** −50 **7 a** 624 **b** 217 **8 a** 102 **b** 791

Homework 3D

1 1.8 **2** 8.5 **3** 16.5 **4** $\frac{23}{3}$ **5** 0.75 **6** $\frac{10}{3}$ **7** 4 **8** $\frac{8}{3}$ **9** $\frac{19}{3}$ **10** $\frac{60}{7}$ **11** 6.5 **12** 4.4 **13** $\frac{13}{3}$
14 0.75 **15** $\frac{8}{3}$ **16** $\frac{16}{7}$ **17** 1.4 **18** $\frac{19}{4}$ **19** 23.5 **20** $\frac{5}{9}$ **21** $\frac{4}{3}$ **22** $\frac{4}{5}$ **23** 2 **24** 1.5

Homework 3E

1 12 **2** 12 **3** 35 **4** 24 **5** 35 **6** 20 **7** 4 **8** 32 **9** 18 **10** 28 **11** 54 **12** 64 **13** 6 **14** 6.4
15 18.75 **16** 12 **17** 4.2 **18** $\frac{40}{3}$ **19** $-\frac{7}{8}$ **20** $-\frac{8}{5}$

Homework 3F

1 −0.5 **2** −0.8 **3** $-\frac{7}{4}$ **4** −5.5 **5** −0.8 **6** $-\frac{1}{8}$ **7** $-\frac{15}{8}$ **8** −0.4 **9** 1 **10** −2 **11** 18 **12** 15 **13** 8
14 −0.6 **15** 5.75 **16** $\frac{17}{8}$ **17** −0.6 **18** −4 **19** −2.75 **20** −1.5

Homework 3G

1 −1　**2** 10　**3** 2　**4** 1.5　**5** 2.4　**6** 3.1　**7** 6.75　**8** 3　**9** $-\frac{5}{12}$　**10** 2.6　**11** 2.1　**12** $-\frac{2}{3}$　**13** 2.8　**14** 4
15 7.25　**16** $\frac{11}{6}$　**17** −5.25　**18** −3　**19** −0.6　**20** $\frac{59}{12}$　**21** 0.1　**22** −2.5　**23** $\frac{23}{24}$　**24** −2

Homework 3H

1 a 2 and 3　**b** 3 and 4　**c** 9 and 10　**d** 6 and 7　**2 a** 2.9　**b** 4.6　**c** 7.9　**d** 5.8
3 a 1 and 2　**b** 3 and 4　**c** 4 and 5　**d** 4 and 5　**4 a** 3.2　**b** 4.6　**c** 5.4　**d** 7.0　**5** 3.5　**6** 4.7

Homework 3 I

1 10.7 and 18.7 cm　**2** 21.8 and 36.8 m　**3** 5.4 and 7.4 cm　**4** 12.6 and 9.6 cm　**5** 7.9　**6** 3.5　**7** 2.8

Homework 3J

1 $x = 3, y = 2$　**2** $x = 5, y = 1$　**3** $x = 3, y = 2$　**4** $x = 5, y = -0.5$　**5 a** $x + y = 16, x - y = 9$　**b** $x = 12.5, y = 3.5$

Homework 3K

1 $x = 2, y = 3$　**2** $x = 7, y = 3$　**3** $x = 2, y = 5$　**4** $x = 4, y = 3$　**5 a** $4x + 3y = 335, 3x + y = 220,$　**b** $x = 65, y = 25, £4.25$

Homework 3L

1 $x = 3, y = 1$　**2** $x = 7, y = 2$　**3** $x = 2.5, y = 3$　**4** $x = 7, y = -1$
5 a $2x + 3y = 2850, 3x + 2y = 3150$　**b** $x = £7.50, y = £4.50$

Homework 3M

1 $x = 3, y = -2$　**2** $x = 2.5, y = -0.5$　**3** $x = 5, y = -3$　**4** $x = 2.5, y = -1$　**5** $x = -3, y = 5.5$　**6** $x = 0.2, y = 1.1$
7 $x = 2.5, y = 1.25$　**8** $x = 1.2, y = 0.2$　**9 a** $x + y = 50, 3x + 4.5y = 183$　**b** 28 @ £3 and 22 @ £4.50

Homework 3N

1 CD £10.50, book £3.50　**2** £1.91　**3** £1.21　**4** 11.5 kg　**5** 12 g in cakes and 13 g in peanuts　**6** £816.25

Homework 3P

1 i $c = y - mx$　**ii** $x = \dfrac{y - c}{m}$　**2 i** $u = v + 10t$　**ii** $t = \dfrac{u - v}{10}$　**3 i** $x = \dfrac{T - 3y}{2}$　**ii** $y = \dfrac{T - 2x}{3}$　**4** $q = \sqrt{p}$

5 $q = \sqrt{(p + 3)}$　**6** $b = \sqrt{(a - c)}$　**7 a** 61.2 m/s　**b** $t = \dfrac{v - u}{g}$　**c** 8.4 secs

Chapter 4

Homework 4A

1 5 cm　**2** 4.41 cm　**3** 10.6 cm　**4** 35.4 cm　**5** 20 cm　**6** 19.2 cm　**7 a** 40.15 m　**b** 2100 m³

Homework 4B

1 a 23.7 cm　**b** 22.2 cm　**c** 6.9 cm　**d** 32.6 cm　**e** 8.1 cm　**f** 760 m　**g** 0.87 cm　**h** 12 m
2 a 10 m　**b** 27.2 cm　**c** 29.4 m　**d** 12.4 cm　**3** 6.7 m

Homework 4C

1 9 m　**2** 3.23 m　**3** 14.14 m　**4** 10 km　**5** 3.22 km　**6** 7.9 m　**b** 3.9 m　**7** $\sqrt{2}$　**8** 12 cm²　**9** Yes $61^2 = 60^2 + 11^2$
10 14.76 units　**11 a** 1 cm represents 2.5 km　**b** 40.4 km

Homework 4D

1 32.8 cm² 9.16 cm²　**2** 36.7 cm²　**3** 43.3 cm²　**4 a** 173.2 cm　**b** Only lengths have doubled. Area has quadrupled.
5 b 8, 8, 6 has area 22.25 cm² and 6, 6, 8 has 17.9 cm²　**6** 54.5 mm²

Homework 4E

1 a i 12.8 cm　**ii** 11.7 cm　**iii** 10 cm　**b** 14.14 cm　**2** Yes, max length 7.35 m　**3 a** 21 cm and 18.4 cm　**b** 13.4 cm
4 a 14.14 m　**b** 14.46 m　**5 a** 11.2 cm　**b** 7.07 cm　**c** 11.2 cm　**d** 12.25 cm　**6 a** 9.9 cm　**b** 10.9 cm　**c** 11.48 cm
7 a Yes, $41^2 = 40^2 + 9^2$　**b** 41.98 cm

Homework 4F

1 a 0.788　**b** 0.719　**c** 0.972　**d** 1　**2 a** 0.616　**b** 0.695　**c** 0.237　**d** 0　**3 a** 1　**b** 1　**c** 1　**d** 1　**e** All 1
4 a 1.280　**b** 1.036　**c** 4.102　**d** 0　**5 a** 1.280　**b** 1.036　**c** 4.102　**d** 0　**e** same
6 a 4.915　**b** 4.950　**c** 11.967　**d** 15.626　**7 a** 7.325　**b** 9.899　**c** 14.123　**d** 25.60
8 $\sin x = \frac{5}{13}$, $\cos x = \frac{12}{13}$, $\tan x = \frac{5}{12}$　**9** $\frac{5}{3}$

Homework 4G

1 a 23.6° **b** 45.0° **c** 61.5° **d** 41.8° **2 a** 66.4° **b** 45.0° **c** 28.5° **d** 70.5°
3 a 21.8° **b** 51.1° **c** 41.2° **d** 69.1° **4 a** 22° **b** 19.5° **c** 17.5° **d** 38.7°
5 a 68° **b** 70.5° **c** 72.5° **d** 51.3 **6 a** 20.6° **b** 56.3° **c** 35.5° **d** 75.3° **7** 36°

Homework 4H

1 a 15.7 **b** 21.3° **c** 80.9° **d** 18.6° **e** 30° **f** 97.1 **2 a** 3.5 **b** 40 **c** 17.5 **3 a** 11.5 km **b** 230°

Homework 4 I

1 a 67.4° **b** 11.3 **c** 42.8° **d** 20.5° **e** 72.1 **f** 54.1° **2 a** 14 **b** 45 **c** 3.5 **3 a** 6.71 km **b** 48.2°

Homework 4J

1 a 15.3 **b** 4.6 **c** 53.4° **d** 7.64 **e** 29.1° **f** 29.9 **2 a** 6 **b** 30 **c** $\frac{10}{3}$ **3** 81.5°

Homework 4K

1 a 65.0° **b** 14.9 **c** 153.3 **d** 26.7° **e** 327 **f** 49.3° **g** 48.2° **h** 230 **i** 45.8 **2** 6 cm **3 a** 9.4 m **b** 65.9°

Homework 4L

1 70.3° **2** 2.74 m to 1.39 m **3** 54 m **4** 5.04 m **5** 29° **6 a** 58.2° **b** 7.75 m

Homework 4M

1 13.5 km **2** 115 m **3** 8.5 m **4** 29.5° **5** 31° **6** 0.4° **7 a** 64 m **b** 9.1°

Homework 4N

1 a 78.2 km **b** 33.2 km **2 a** 10.3° **b** 190.3° **3** 128.7° **4** 3.94 km
5 a 67.8 km **b** 15.9 km **c** 17.0 km **d** 168.6° **6 a ii** 226° **b** 170 km **c i** 28.1° **ii** 344.1°

Homework 4P

1 9.59 cm **2** 20.4° **3** 17.4 m **4 a** 30.1 cm² **b** 137.2 cm² **5** 63.6 cm² 59.7 cm²

Chapter 5

Homework 5A

1 a 900° **b** 1620° **c** 3240° **d** 5940° **2 a** 156° **b** 160° **c** 168° **d** 176.4° **3 a** 10 **b** 16 **c** 36 **d** 40
4 a 18 **b** 12 **c** 20 **d** 90 **5 a** 8 **b** 24 **c** 36 **d** 15 **6** Octagon **7 a** Decagon **b** 115°

Homework 5B

1 $a = 62°, b = 108°, c = 58°, d = 122°, e = 58°, f = 15°, g = 161°$ **2** $x = 50°, y = 40°, x = 11°, y = 40°$
3 a $x = 100°$, Trapezium **b** $x = 50°$, Kite **4 a** 360

Homework 5C

1 a 23° **b** 84° **c** 200° **d** 54° **e** 62° **f** 60° **2 a** 19° **b** 27° **c** 49° **3 a** 78° **b** 29° **c** 78°
4 a $x = 20°, y = 105°$ **b** $x = 10°, y = 36°$ **6 a** 89° **b** 46°

Homework 5D

1 a $a = 68°, b = 100°$ **b** $d = 98°, e = 98°, f = 82°$ **c** $d = 95°, e = 111°$ **d** $n = 142°, m = 118°$
2 a 89° **b** 98° **c** $x = 82°, y = 33°$ **3 a** $x = 52°, y = 104°$ **b** $x = 120°, y = 120°$ **c** $x = 95°, y = 75°$
3 BAC = 180 − ACD (co-interior), ABD = 180 − ACD (opposite in cyclic quad), Hence BAC = ABD

Homework 5E

1 a 48° **b** 30° **2 a** 4 cm **b** 9.2 cm **3 a** $x = 16°, y = 74°$ **b** $x = 80°, y = 50°$ **4 a** 18° **b** 16°
5 a 42° **b** 138°

Homework 5F

1 $a = 68°, b = 62°, c = 50°, d = 83°, e = 55°, f = 42°$ **2 a** 50° **b** 63° **3 a** $x = 36°, y = 36°$ **b** $x = 70°, y = 70°$
4 a 18° **b** $x = 48°, y = 70°, z = 62°$ **5** $x = 68°, y = 22°, z = 31°$

Chapter 6

▰▰ Homework 6A

1 a Yes SAS   **b** Yes SSS   **c** Yes ASA

▰▰ Homework 6B

1 i $\binom{7}{1}$ **ii** $\binom{10}{-2}$ **iii** $\binom{3}{-2}$ **iv** $\binom{-7}{-1}$ **v** $\binom{3}{-3}$ **vi** $\binom{-4}{-3}$

2

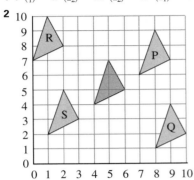

3 a $\binom{1}{-5}$ **b** $\binom{-8}{6}$ **c** $\binom{1}{-5}$ **d** $\binom{6}{4}$ **e** $\binom{7}{-1}$ **f** $\binom{7}{-1}$ **g** $\binom{8}{-6}$ **h** $\binom{-6}{-4}$

▰▰ Homework 6C

1 a

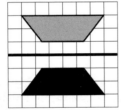

b

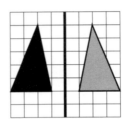

c

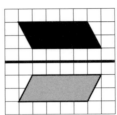

d

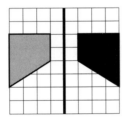

e

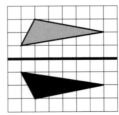

f

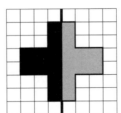

2 f Reflection in $y = -x$

c Congruent

3

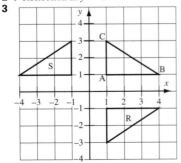

4 f Reflection in y-axis

Homework 6D

1

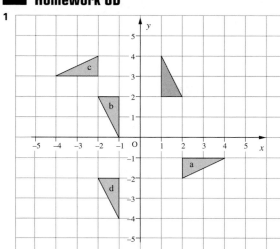

2
a rotation 90° anti-clockwise about (0, 0)
b rotation 180° (anti-)clockwise about (0, 0)
c rotation 90° clockwise about (2.5, 0.5)
d rotation 180° (anti-)clockwise about (2, −1)

3

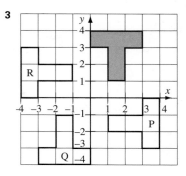

d rotation 90° clockwise about O

4 **a** (1, 1), (3, 1), (3, 3), (1, 3)   **b** (1, −1), (3, −1), (3, −3), (1, −3)   **c** (−1, −1), (−3, −1), (−3, −3), (−1, −3)
d (−1, 1), (−3, 1), (−3, 3), (−1, 3)   **e** Same numbers different signs

Homework 6F

1 **a** reflection in *x*-axis   **b** reflection in *y*-axis   **c** translation of $\binom{6}{-1}$ **d** rotation of 180° (anti-)clockwise about (0, 0)

e rotation of 90° clockwise about (0, 0)   **f** reflection in $y = -x$ **g** reflection in $y = x$

2 **e** 90° clockwise about (0, 0)   **3** (−5, −2)

Chapter 7

Homework 7A

5

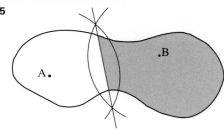

Homework 7B

5 **e** AC = 5.9 cm, BC = 7.2 cm   **6** **b** BC = 3 cm

Homework 7C

1

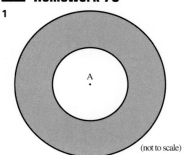

(not to scale)

2 a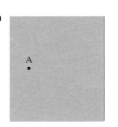

b

3 Sphere radius 1 metre

4 a 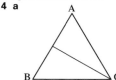   **b** 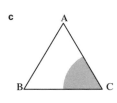   **c** 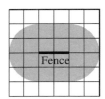   **d**

5   **6** 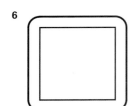   **7**

▬ Homework 7D

1 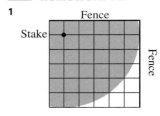   **2**   **3**

4 b No   **c** No   **5** No   **6 b** No

Chapter 8

▬ Homework 8A

1 a 5^4 **b** 7^5 **c** 19^3 **d** 4^5 **e** 1^7 **f** 8^5 **g** 6^1 **h** 11^6 **i** 0.9^4 **j** 999^3

2 a $4 \times 4 \times 4 \times 4 \times 4$ **b** $8 \times 8 \times 8 \times 8$ **c** $5 \times 5 \times 5$ **d** $9 \times 9 \times 9 \times 9 \times 9 \times 9$ **e** $1 \times 1 \times 1 \times 1 \times 1 \times 1 \times 1 \times 1 \times 1 \times 1 \times 1$
f $7 \times 7 \times 7$ **g** $5.2 \times 5.2 \times 5.2$ **h** $7.5 \times 7.5 \times 7.5$ **i** $7.7 \times 7.7 \times 7.7 \times 7.7$ **j** $10\,000 \times 10\,000 \times 10\,000$

3 a 625   **b** 16807   **c** 6859   **d** 1024   **e** 1   **f** 32768   **g** 6   **h** 1771561   **i** 0.6561   **j** 997002999

4 a 1024   **b** 4096   **c** 125   **d** 531441   **e** 1   **f** 343   **g** 140.608   **h** 421.875   **i** 3515.3041   **j** 1000000000000

5 a 1   **b** 9   **c** 1   **d** 1   **e** 100000   **6 a** −8   **b** −1   **c** 81   **d** −125   **e** 1000000

7 a 16   **b** −125   **c** 81   **d** −32   **e** 1

▬ Homework 8B

1 a $\frac{1}{25}$ **b** $\frac{1}{4}$ **c** $\frac{1}{1000}$ **d** $\frac{1}{27}$ **e** $\frac{1}{x^2}$ **f** $\frac{5}{t}$ **2 a** 2^{-4} **b** 7^{-1} **c** x^{-2}

3 a i 2^5 **ii** 2^{-2} **b i** 10^5 **ii** 10^{-2} **c i** 5^4 **ii** 5^{-3}

4 a i 9   **ii** $\frac{4}{3}$ **b i** $\frac{1}{25}$ **ii** $\frac{1}{125}$ **c i** $\frac{1}{8}$ **ii** 1   **5 a** $1\frac{1}{2}$ **b** $\frac{17}{72}$

Homework 8C

1 a 7^5 **b** 7^9 **c** 7^7 **d** 7^6 **e** 7^{14} **f** 7^8 **2 a** 5^4 **b** 5^6 **c** 5^1 **d** 5^0 **e** 5^2
3 a a^3 **b** a^5 **c** a^7 **d** a^4 **e** a^2 **f** a **4 a** $15a^6$ **b** $21a^5$ **c** $30a^6$ **d** $12a^9$ **e** $125a^8$
5 a $4a^3$ **b** $3a^5$ **c** $5a^5$ **d** $8a^9$ **e** $3a^8$ **f** $6a^{-4}$ **6 a** $12a^6b^3$ **b** $14a^4b^8$ **c** $20a^7b^4$ **d** $3a^2b^4$ **e** $4ab^8$

7 Let $x = 0$ and $y = 1$, so $a^0 \div a^1 = \dfrac{1}{a} = a^{0-1} = a^{-1}$

Homework 8D

1 6 **2** 12 **3** 5 **4** 14 **5** 2 **6** 5 **7** 0.5 **8** $\frac{1}{12}$ **9** $\frac{1}{3}$ **10** $\frac{5}{9}$ **11** 1.5 **12** 0.75 **13** $\frac{2}{3}$ **14** 0.4
15 1.5 **16** 1.25 **17** 1.5 **18 a** 9 **b** 2 **c** 0.25

Homework 8E

1 a 8 **b** 625 **c** 27 **2 a** $t^{\frac{3}{4}}$ **b** $m^{\frac{2}{3}}$ **3 a** 9 **b** 16 **c** 216 **d** 243
4 a

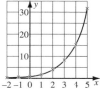

b 6 **5 a** 2.285 **b** 0.301 **6 a** 2 **b** 2^{-5} **c** $\frac{1}{5}$

Homework 8F

1 a 350 **b** 21.5 **c** 6740 **d** 46.3 **e** 301.45 **f** 78 560 **g** 642 **h** 0.67 **i** 85 **j** 79 800 **k** 658 **l** 21 530
m 889 000 **n** 35 214.7 **o** 37 284.1 **p** 34 280 000
2 a 45.38 **b** 43.5 **c** 76.459 **d** 64.37 **e** 42.287 **f** 0.2784 **g** 2.465 **h** 7.63 **i** 0.076 **j** 0.008 97
k 0.0865 **l** 0.015 **m** 0.000 000 879 9 **n** 0.234 **o** 7.654 **p** 0.000 073 2
3 a 120 000 **b** 200 000 **c** 14 000 **d** 21 000 **e** 900 **f** 125 000 **g** 40 000 **h** 6000 **i** 14 000 **j** 300 000
k 7500 **l** 140 000
4 a 5 **b** 300 **c** 35 **d** 40 **e** 3 **f** 150 **g** 14 **h** 50 **i** 6 **j** 15 **k** 4 **l** 200
5 a 730 **b** 329 000 **c** 7940 **d** 68 000 000 **e** 0.034 6 **f** 0.000 507 **g** 0.000 23 **h** 0.000 89

Homework 8G

1 a 350 **b** 41.5 **c** 0.005 7 **d** 14.6 **e** 0.038 9 **f** 4600 **g** 270 **h** 86 **i** 4600 **j** 397 000 **k** 0.003 65
l 705
2 a 7.8×10^2 **b** 4.35×10^1 **c** 6.78×10^4 **d** 7.4×10^9 **e** 3.078×10^{10} **f** 4.278×10^{-4} **g** 6.45×10^3
h 4.7×10^2 **i** 1.2×10^{-4} **j** 9.643×10^1 **k** 7.478×10 **l** 4.1578×10^{-3}
3 $1.99 \times 10^3, 2.4673 \times 10^7$ **4** $2.001 \times 10^3, 1.5282 \times 10^4$ **5** $1.99 \times 10^3, 6.13 \times 10^{11}$ **6** $9.3 \times 10^7, 2.4 \times 10^{13}$ **7** 6.5×10^{-13}

Homework 8H

1 a 2.8×10^{16} **b** 3.5×10^{13} **c** 2.4×10^4 **d** 1.05 **2 a** 3×10^4 **b** 3×10^3 **c** 5×10^6 **d** 1.4×10^{-1}
3 a 2×10^2 **b** 4×10^2 **c** 4×10^{10} **4 a** 1.6×10^{13} **b** 4×10^{-2} **c** 2.08×10^7 **d** 1.92×10^7 **e** 2.5×10
5 a 8×10^{-5} **b** 5 **c** 2.4×10^{-2} **d** -1.6×10^{-2} **e** 2×10^{-1}

Homework 8 I

1 a yes **b** no **c** no **d** yes **e** no **2 a** $\sqrt{15}$ **b** $\sqrt{30}$ **3 a** $-\sqrt{7}$ **b** π **c** $-\sqrt{3}$ **4 a** $\sqrt{8}$ **b** π

Homework 8J

1 a 0.75 **b** $0.0\dot{6}$ **c** 0.04 **d** $0.0\dot{9}$ **e** 0.05
2 a $\frac{4}{13} = 0.\dot{3}0769\dot{2}$ $\frac{5}{13} = 0.\dot{3}8461\dot{5}$ $\frac{6}{13} = 0.\dot{4}6153\dot{8}$ $\frac{7}{13} = 0.\dot{5}3846\dot{1}$ $\frac{8}{13} = 0.\dot{6}1538\dot{4}$ $\frac{9}{13} = 0.\dot{6}9230\dot{7}$ $\frac{10}{13} = 0.\dot{7}6923\dot{0}$ $\frac{11}{13} = 0.\dot{8}4615\dot{3}$
$\frac{12}{13} = 0.\dot{9}2307\dot{6}$ **b** repeating numbers are cyclic and belong to one of two sets of numbers
3 $\frac{1}{5}$ $\frac{2}{9}$ $\frac{23}{100}$ $\frac{3}{11}$ $\frac{1}{7}$ **4 a** $\frac{57}{100}$ **b** $\frac{11}{40}$ **c** $\frac{17}{20}$ **d** $\frac{3}{50}$ **e** $3\frac{13}{20}$ **5 a** 2.424242 **b** 2.4 **c** 24 **d** $\frac{24}{990}$ **e** $\frac{4}{165}$
6 a $\frac{7}{9}$ **b** $\frac{19}{33}$ **c** $\frac{6}{11}$ **d** $\frac{275}{999}$ **e** $2\frac{5}{9}$ **f** $2\frac{4}{11}$ **g** $\frac{7}{110}$ **h** $2\frac{5}{66}$ **7 a** $\frac{17}{10}$ **b i** $17.\dot{7}$ **ii** 16 **iii** $\frac{16}{9}$

Homework 8K

1 a $2\sqrt{3}$ **b** $\sqrt{35}$ **c** 5 **d** 8 **2 a** $\sqrt{3}$ **b** 3 **c** 4 **d** $\sqrt{(\frac{3}{2})}$ **3 a** $3\sqrt{2}$ **b** $5\sqrt{15}$ **c** $8\sqrt{2}$ **d** $4\sqrt{5}$
4 a $2\sqrt{3}$ **b** 3 **c** $4\sqrt{2}$ **d** $3\sqrt{3}$ **5 a** $3\sqrt{10}$ **b** $4\sqrt{2}$ **c** $3\sqrt{7}$ **d** $10\sqrt{3}$ **e** $5\sqrt{6}$ **f** $3\sqrt{30}$ **g** $4\sqrt{6}$ **h** $5\sqrt{5}$
6 a 80 **b** 32 **c** 120 **d** 36 **e** $10\sqrt{15}$ **f** 18 **g** 24 **h** 36 **i** $8\sqrt{2}$ **j** 9 **k** 15 **l** 1 **m** $5\sqrt{2}$ **n** 9 **o** 15
7 a 80 **b** 48 **c** 5 **8** $a = 3, b = 4. \sqrt{(a^2 + b^2)} = 5. a + b = 7$ **9 a** $\frac{2}{9}$ **b** $\frac{16}{3}$ **10 a** $3\sqrt{8}$ **b** 16 **c** $9\sqrt{2}$

Homework 8L

2 a $3\sqrt{5} - \sqrt{10}$ **b** $3\sqrt{8} - 16$ **c** $24 + 12\sqrt{8}$ **d** $-1 - \sqrt{3}$ **e** $1 - \sqrt{5}$ **f** $8 + 2\sqrt{2}$ **3 a** $\sqrt{15}$ cm **b** 2 cm
4 a $\sqrt{2}$ cm^2 **b** $2\sqrt{3} + \sqrt{21}$ cm^2

5 a $\sqrt{7}/7$ **b** $\sqrt{2}/4$ **c** $2\frac{\sqrt{5}}{5}$ **d** $\frac{\sqrt{2}}{4}$ **e** $\frac{5}{3}$ **f** $2\frac{\sqrt{6}}{3}$ **g** $\dfrac{(\sqrt{3} + 3)}{3}$ **h** $\dfrac{(3\sqrt{8} - 4)}{8}$

6 a i 22 **ii** 34 **b i** $\dfrac{(25 + 5\sqrt{3})}{22}$ **ii** $\dfrac{(12 + 6\sqrt{3} - 2\sqrt{2} - \sqrt{6})}{34}$ **7 a i** -24 **ii** $\sqrt{5}$ **iii** $-\frac{1}{343}$ **b** $21 - 8\sqrt{5}$

Chapter 9

■ Homework 9A

1 a mode = 16, median = 15, mean = 15.3   **b** mode = 5, median = 5, mean = 4.67   **2 a** 289   **b** 2   **c** 142   **d** 1.7

■ Homework 9B

1 99 97 95 92 89 88 93 90 95 99 103 103 107 102 103 97 102 104 105 103 106 112
Students should plot these data in a suitable form.
2 a 35 62 69 50 45 75 101 70 62 66 81 54 38 49 66 104 111 112
Students should plot these data in a suitable form.
b Average is increasing but scores very variable.

■ Homework 9C

1 a i 61–80   **ii** 58   **b i** 20.01–30.00   **ii** £27.40   **2 a** 79   **b** 35 minutes   **c** mode   **d** 94%

■ Homework 9D

1 i

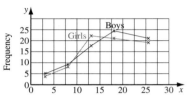

ii boys 16.7 girls 16.5 little difference   **2 i** 2.258   **ii** discrete data

■ Homework 9E

1 a

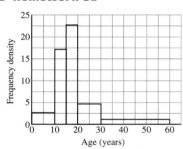

b

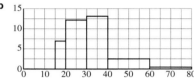

c Average age at the second show was higher.

2 a

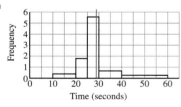

b 28.55 seconds   **d** Area on both sides is same.

3 a

$0 < t \leq 5$	25
$5 < t \leq 10$	37.5
$10 < t \leq 20$	100
$20 < t \leq 30$	50
$30 < t \leq 35$	37.5
$35 < t \leq 40$	12.5

b 18 min   **4**

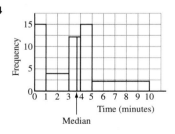

■ Homework 9F

1 a Sheet should include a section on the time at which survey done, how many times a week videos are hired, what is the latest time you use the shop, etc.?
b Yes. Late night is likely to get a more positive response.
2 a Sheet should include a section on
Do you use a youth club now?
What activities would you want? etc.
and space for tallies and a column to record the totals.
3 Sheet should inlcude list of types of films, space for tallies and a column for the totals.

Homework 9G

1 You should include questions such as
How old are you?   Do you drink alcohol?   If so how many times a week?   Do you tell your parents if you have been drinking?
2 You should include questions such as
Do you use the internet?   If so how many times a week?
3 You should include questions such as
How old are you?   Do you watch TV?   If so how many times a week?
4 You should include questions such as
Record of gender   How many people are in your household?   What are their genders?
How many times a week do you shop for groceries?

Homework 9H

1 You will need to pick a sample from all ages. You will need to ask proportionate numbers of boys and girls. You must ask people with different interests as sporty people may want to finish earlier.
2 a Likely to have an interest in religion so opinions may be biased
  b This would be quite reliable as the sample is likely to be representative
  c Younger children will not like the same sort of games as older pupils so sample is likely to give a biased result.
3 a this is quite a good method. The sample is not random but should give reliable results.
  b Not very reliable as people at a shopping centre are not likely to be sporty. Better to ask a random sample at different venues and different times.
  c Not everyone has a phone; people don't like being asked in the evening. Need to do other samples such as asking people in the street.
4 a About 10% of population
  b

Year	Boys	Girls	Total
7	16	14	30
8	16	16	32
9	14	16	30
10	15	16	31
11	13	14	27
Total	74	76	150

5 Not everyone has a phone.
People may not travel by train every week.
200 may not be a big enough sample.

Chapter 10

Homework 10A

1 $12t$ **2** $10y$ **3** $8y$ **4** $9w$ **5** $4t^2$ **6** $6b^2$ **7** $3w^2$ **8** $12y^2$ **9** $5p^2$ **10** $128t^2$ **11** $20m^2$ **12** $24t^2$ **13** $7mt$
14 $5yw$ **15** $8qt$ **16** $69nt$ **17** $30q$ **18** $10f$ **19** $18k$ **20** $35r$ **21** t^3 **22** p^3 **23** $5m^3$ **24** $3t^3$ **25** $8n^3$
26 $20r^3$ **27** t^4 **28** k^5 **29** $16n^5$ **30** $12t^7$ **31** $14a^7$ **32** $3k^7$ **33** k^3 **34** $10y^2$ **35** $18d^3$ **36** $-12p^6$
37 $5mq^2$ **38** $12m^2y$ **39** $12m^2t$ **40** $10q^2p^2$

Homework 10B

1 $12 + 3m$ **2** $18 + 6p$ **3** $16 - 4y$ **4** $18 + 21k$ **5** $12 - 20f$ **6** $8 - 46w$ **7** $7g + 7h$ **8** $8k + 16m$ **9** $12d - 6n$
10 $t^2 + 5t$ **11** $m^2 + 4m$ **12** $k^2 - 2k$ **13** $4g^2 + g$ **14** $3y^2 - 21y$ **15** $7p - 8p^2$ **16** $2m^2 + 10m$ **17** $3t^2 - 6t$
18 $15k - 3k^2$ **19** $8g^2 + 6g$ **20** $8h^2 - 12h$ **21** $12t - 10t^2$ **22** $12d^2 + 20de$ **23** $12y^2 + 5ky$ **24** $18m^3 - 6m^2p$
25 $y^3 + 7y$ **26** $h^4 + 9h$ **27** $k^3 - 4k$ **28** $3t^3 + 9t$ **29** $5h^4 - 10h$ **30** $4g^4 - 12g$ **31** $10m^3 + 5m^2$ **32** $8d^3 - 2d^4$
33 $12w^3 + 4wt$ **34** $15a^3 - 3ab$ **35** $14p^4 - 16mp$ **36** $3m^2 + 5m^3$ **37** $4t^4$ **38** $4g^2t - 3g^4$ **39** $14t^3 + 2mt^2$
40 $12h^3 + 15gh^2$

Homework 10C

1 a $9t$ **b** $7m$ **c** $7y$ **d** $10d$ **e** $2e$ **f** $3g$ **g** $2p$ **h** $4t$ **i** $5t^2$ **j** $3y^2$ **k** $7ab$ **l** a^2d
2 a $18 + 7t$ **b** $22 + 24k$ **c** $13 + 32m$ **d** $17 + 13y$ **e** $28 + 12f$ **f** $20 + 33g$
3 a $2 + 2h$ **b** $9g + 5$ **c** $6y + 11$ **d** $7t - 4$ **e** $17k + 16$ **f** $6e + 20$
4 a $5m + 2p + 2mp$ **b** $4k + 5h + 3hk$ **c** $t + 3n + 7nt$ **d** $p + 5q + 8pq$ **e** $6h + 12j + 11hj$ **f** $15y + 2t + 20ty$
5 a $4t^2 + 13t$ **b** $15y^2 + 7y$ **c** $11w^2 + 22w$ **d** $17p^2 + 6p$ **e** $m^2 + 8m$ **f** $14d - 3d^2$
6 a $2a^3 + 10a^2 + 15ab + 3ac$ **b** $4y^3 + 3y^2 + 12yw - 4ty$

Homework 10D

1 $3(3m + 4t)$ **2** $3(3t + 2p)$ **3** $4(m + 3k)$ **4** $2(2r + 3t)$ **5** $m(2n + 3)$ **6** $g(4g + 3)$ **7** $4(w - 2t)$ **8** $2(5p - 3k)$
9 $2(6h - 5k)$ **10** $2m(2p + k)$ **11** $2b(2c + 3k)$ **12** $4a(2b + c)$ **13** $y(3y + 4)$ **14** $t(5t - 3)$ **15** $d(3d - 2)$
16 $3m(2m - p)$ **17** $3p(p + 3t)$ **18** $4p(2t + 3m)$ **19** $2b(4a - 3c)$ **20** $4a(a - 2b)$ **21** $2t(4m - 3p)$ **22** $4at(5t + 3)$
23 $2bc(2b - 5)$ **24** $2b(2ac + 3ed)$ **25** $2(3a^2 + 2a + 5)$ **26** $3b(4a + 2c + 3d)$ **27** $t(6t + 3 + a)$ **28** $3mt(32t - 1 + 23m)$
29 $2ab(3b + 1 - 2a)$ **30** $5pt(t + 3 + p)$ **31** DNF **32** $m(3 + 2p)$ **33** $t(t - 5)$ **34** DNF **35** $2m(4m - 3p)$
36 DNF **37** $a(3a - 7b)$ **38** DNF **39** $b(7a - 4bc)$ **40** DNF **41** $3mt(2m + 3t)$ **42** DNF

Homework 10E

1 $x^2 + 7x + 10$ **2** $t^2 + 5t + 6$ **3** $w^2 + 5w + 4$ **4** $m^2 + 8m + 12$ **5** $k^2 + 6k + 8$ **6** $a^2 + 4a + 3$ **7** $x^2 + 2x - 3$
8 $t^2 + 2t - 24$ **9** $w^2 - w - 6$ **10** $f^2 - 3f - 4$ **11** $g^2 - 3g - 10$ **12** $y^2 + 3y - 10$ **13** $x^2 - x - 12$ **14** $p^2 - p - 6$
15 $k^2 - 4k - 5$ **16** $y^2 + 3y - 18$ **17** $a^2 + 2a - 8$ **18** $t^2 + t - 20$ **19** $x^2 - 5x + 6$ **20** $r^2 - 5r + 4$ **21** $m^2 - 8m + 7$
22 $g^2 - 8g + 15$ **23** $h^2 - 8h + 12$ **24** $n^2 - 10n + 16$ **25** $x^2 + 7x + 12$ **26** $20 - t - t^2$ **27** $12 - 4b - b^2$
28 $35 - 12y + y^2$ **29** $p^2 + p - 6$ **30** $8k - 15 - k^2$

Homework 10F

1 $12x^2 + 22x + 8$ **2** $6y^2 + 7y + 2$ **3** $12t^2 + 30t + 12$ **4** $6t^2 + t - 2$ **5** $18m^2 - 9m - 2$ **6** $20k^2 - 3k - 9$ **7** $12p^2 + p - 20$
8 $18w^2 + 27w + 4$ **9** $15a^2 - 17a - 4$ **10** $15r^2 - 11r + 2$ **11** $12g^2 - 11g + 2$ **12** $12d^2 - 5d - 2$ **13** $15 + 32p + 16p^2$
14 $15 + 19t + 6t^2$ **15** $2 + 11p + 15p^2$ **16** $21 - 2t - 8t^2$ **17** $20 + 3n - 2n^2$ **18** $20f^2 + 11f - 3$ **19** $10 - 7q - 12q^2$
20 $6 + 7p - 3p^2$ **21** $5 + 17t - 12t^2$ **22** $15 - 32r + 16r^2$ **23** $4 - 21x + 5x^2$ **24** $25m - 6 - 14m^2$ **25** $3x^2 + 8xy + 5y^2$
26 $12y^2 - 13yt - 4t^2$ **27** $25x^2 - 10xy - 3y^2$ **28** $x^2 - 5xy + 6y^2$ **29** $4m^2 + 17mp - 15p^2$ **30** $3t^2 - 13kt + 4k^2$

Homework 10G

1 $x^2 - 1$ **2** $t^2 - 4$ **3** $y^2 - 9$ **4** $4m^2 - 9$ **5** $16k^2 - 9$ **6** $25h^2 - 1$ **7** $9 - 4x^2$ **8** $49 - 4t^2$ **9** $16 - 25y^2$
10 $a^2 - b^2$ **11** $9t^2 - k^2$ **12** $m^2 - 9p^2$ **13** $64k^2 - g^2$ **14** $a^2c^2 - b^2d^2$ **15** $x^4 - y^4$

Homework 10H

1 $x^2 + 8x + 16$ **2** $m^2 + 6m + 9$ **3** $25 + 10t + t^2$ **4** $4 + 4p + p^2$ **5** $m2 - 4m + 4$ **6** $t^2 - 8t + 16$ **7** $9 - 6m + m^2$
8 $36 - 12k + k^2$ **9** $4x^2 + 4x + 1$ **10** $9t^2 + 12t + 4$ **11** $1 + 8y + 16y^2$ **12** $4 + 4m + m^2$ **13** $9t^2 - 12t + 4$
14 $4x^2 - 4x + 1$ **15** $1 - 8t + 16t^2$ **16** $25 - 40r + 16r^2$ **17** $a^2 + 2ab + b^2$ **18** $x^2 - 2xy + y^2$ **19** $9t^2 + 6ty + y^2$
20 $m^2 - 4mn + 4n^2$ **21** $x^2 + 6x + 5$ **22** $x^2 - 8x - 9$ **23** $x^2 + 10x - 11$ **24** $x^2 - 2x$

Homework 10 I

1 $(x + 1)(x + 6)$ **2** $(t + 2)(t + 2)$ **3** $(m + 1)(m + 10)$ **4** $(k + 3)(k + 8)$ **5** $(p + 6)(p + 4)$ **6** $(r + 2)(r + 9)$
7 $(w + 3)(w + 6)$ **8** $(x + 2)(x + 6)$ **9** $(a + 12)(a + 1)$ **10** $(k - 3)(k - 7)$ **11** $(f - 1)(f - 21)$ **12** $(b + 32)(b + 3)$
13 $(t + 3)(t + 2)$ **14** $(m - 4)(m - 1)$ **15** $(p - 2)(p - 5)$ **16** $(x - 4)(x - 9)$ **17** $(c - 4)(c - 8)$ **18** $(t - 3)(t - 12)$
19 $(y - 6)(y - 8)$ **20** $(j - 3)(j - 16)$ **21** $(p + 3)(p + 5)$ **22** $(y + 3)(y - 2)$ **23** $(t + 8)(t - 1)$ **24** $(x + 10)(x - 1)$
25 $(m - 4)(m + 3)$ **26** $(r + 7)(r - 1)$ **27** $(n - 9)(n + 2)$ **28** $(m - 22)(m + 2)$ **29** $(w - 8)(w + 3)$ **30** $(t + 10)(t - 9)$
31 $(x - 9)(x + 8)$ **32** $(t - 21)(t + 3)$ **33** $(d - 1)(d - 1)$ **34** $(y + 4)(y + 25)$ **35** $(t - 2)(t - 8)$ **36** $(m - 3)(m - 27)$
37 $(x - 6)(x - 24)$ **38** $(d - 6)(d + 2)$ **39** $(t + 5)(t - 4)$ **40** $(q + 8)(q - 7)$ **41** $(p - 2)(p + 1)$ **42** $(v - 7)(v + 5)$
43 $(t - 3)(t - 1)$ **44** $(m + 4)(m - 1)$

Homework 10J

1 $(x + 9)(x - 9)$ **2** $(t - 6)(t + 6)$ **3** $(2 - x)(2 + x)$ **4** $(9 - t)(9 + t)$ **5** $(k - 20)(k + 20)$ **6** $(8 - y)(8 + y)$ **7** $(x - y)(x + y)$
8 $(a - 3b)(a + 3b)$ **9** $(3x - 5y)(3x + 5y)$ **10** $(3x - 4)(3x + 4)$ **11** $(10t - 2w)(10t + 2w)$ **12** $(6a - 7b)(6a + 7b)$
13 $\dfrac{1}{2a + 3}$

Homework 10K

1 $x = -3, -2$ **2** $t = -4, -1$ **3** $a = -5, -3$ **4** $x = -4, 1$ **5** $x = -2, 5$ **6** $t = -3, 4$ **7** $x = 2, -1$ **8** $x = 1, -4$
9 $a = 6, -5$ **10** $x = 2, 5$ **11** $x = 2, 1$ **12** $a = 2, 6$ **13** $(x + 5)(x + 1) = 0, x = -1, -5$ **14** $(x + 3)(x + 6) = 0, x = -3, -6$
15 $(x - 8)(x + 1) = 0, x = 8, -1$ **16** $(x - 7)(x + 3) = 0, x = 7, -3$ **17** $(x + 5)(x - 2) = 0, x = -5, 2$
18 $(x + 5)(x - 3) = 0, x = -5, 3$ **19** $(t - 6)(t + 2) = 0, t = 6, -2$ **20** $(t - 6)(t + 3) = 0, t = 6, -3$ **21** $(x + 2)(x - 1) = 0, x = -2, 1$
22 $(x - 2)(x - 2) = 0, x = 2$ **23** $(m - 5)(m - 5) = 0, m = 5$ **24** $(t - 8)(t - 2) = 0, t = 8, 2$ **25** $(t + 3)(t + 4) = 0, t = -3, -4$
26 $(k - 6)(k + 3) = 0, k = 6, -3$ **27** $(a - 4)(a - 16) = 0, a = 4, 16$

Homework 10L

1 $(3x + 1)(x + 1)$ **2** $(3x + 1)(x - 1)$ **3** $(2x + 1)(2x + 3)$ **4** $(2x + 1)(x + 3)$ **5** $(5x + 1)(3x + 2)$ **6** $(2x - 1)(2x + 3)$
7 $(3x - 2)(2x - 1)$ **8** $(4x + 2)(2x - 3)$ **9** $(8x + 3)(x - 2)$ **10** $(6x - 1)(x - 2)$ **11 a** $2x(3x - 1)$ **b** $(6x - 1)(x + 2)$

Homework 10M

1 a $(2x + 1)(x + 2) = 0, x = -\frac{1}{2}, -2$ **b** $(7x + 1)(x + 1) = 0, x = -\frac{1}{7}, -1$ **c** $(4x + 7)(x - 1) = 0, x = -\frac{7}{4}, 1$
 d $(3x + 5)(2x + 1) = 0, x = -\frac{5}{3}, -\frac{1}{2}$ **e** $(3x + 2)(2x + 1) = 0, x = -\frac{2}{3}, -\frac{1}{2}$ **2 a** $3, -2$ **b** $-\frac{1}{4}, -\frac{3}{2}$ **c** $6, -5$ **d** $\frac{3}{2}, -7$ **e** $-\frac{3}{4}, 3$
3 a $\dfrac{x + 3}{3}$ **b** $\frac{3}{4}, \frac{4}{3}$

Homework 10N

1 $1.14, -1.47$ **2** $-0.29, -1.71$ **3** $3.19, -2.19$ **4** $0.43, -0.77$ **5** $-0.57, -1.77$ **6** $-0.09, -5.41$ **7** $-0.22, -2.28$
8 $2.16, -4.16$ **9** $1.65, -3.65$ **10** $6.14, -1.14$

Homework 10P

1 a $(x + 5)^2 - 25$ **b** $(x + 9)^2 - 81$ **c** $(x - 4)^2 - 16$ **d** $(x + 10)^2 - 100$ **e** $(x + 3.5)^2 - 12.25$
2 a $(x + 5)^2 - 26$ **b** $(x + 9)^2 - 86$ **c** $(x - 4)^2 - 13$ **d** $(x + 2.5)^2 - 7.25$
3 a $-5 \pm \sqrt{26}$ **b** $-9 \pm \sqrt{86}$ **c** $4 \pm \sqrt{13}$ **d** $-10 \pm \sqrt{93}$ **e** $\frac{5}{2} \pm \sqrt{(\frac{29}{4})}$ **4** $0.36, -8.36$
5 a $(x + 2)^2 - 10$ **b** $x = -2 \pm \sqrt{10}$

Homework 10Q

1 0.29, −0.69 **2** 2.26, −0.59 **3** No solution **4** 1, −1.4 **5** 1, −0.25 **6** 5.32, −1.32 **7** 2.77, −1.27

Homework 10R

1 a $3 \pm \sqrt{13}$ **b** $-1 \pm \sqrt{11}$ **c** $-3 \pm \sqrt{17}$ **d** $-2 \pm \sqrt{10}$ **e** $1 \pm \sqrt{3}$

2 a $\dfrac{-2 \pm \sqrt{10}}{2}$ **b** $\dfrac{-2 \pm \sqrt{10}}{3}$ **c** $\dfrac{-5 \pm \sqrt{73}}{4}$ **d** $\dfrac{5 \pm \sqrt{97}}{6}$ **e** $\dfrac{-1 \pm \sqrt{61}}{6}$ **3 b** $\dfrac{3 \pm \sqrt{5}}{2}$

Homework 10S

1 5, 12, 13 **2** 10 m and 13 m **3** 4.56 and 0.44 **4** $\frac{1}{3}$ and 2 **5** 12 cm **6** 60 mph **7** £1 per kilo

8 a $\dfrac{15}{x} + \dfrac{11}{x-2}$ **b** $\dfrac{15}{x} + \dfrac{11}{x-2} = 4$ **c ii** 7.5 mph

Homework 10T

1 a $\dfrac{7x}{10}$ **b** $\dfrac{17x}{20}$ **c** $\dfrac{5x+5}{6}$ **d** $\dfrac{11x-29}{15}$ **2 a** $\dfrac{3x}{10}$ **b** $\dfrac{7x}{20}$ **c** $\dfrac{-x+5}{6}$ **d** $\dfrac{-x-1}{5}$

3 a $\dfrac{x^2}{10}$ **b** $\dfrac{x^2}{20}$ **c** $\dfrac{3x-6}{x-3}$ **d** $\dfrac{1}{2x}$ **4 a** $\dfrac{5}{2}$ **b** $\dfrac{10x}{9y}$ **c** $\dfrac{x^2-6x+5}{27}$ **d** $\dfrac{1}{2x}$

5 a 5 **b** $\frac{10}{11}$ **c** 4 **7 a** $2, -\frac{3}{2}$ **b** 0, 5 **c** $3, -\frac{7}{3}$ **8 a** $\dfrac{13x}{20}$ **b** $\frac{360}{13} \approx 27.7$

Homework 10U

1 a $x = 4, y = 2$ **b** $x = 3, y = 1$ **2 a** (6, 2), (−1, −12) **b** (2, 6), (−6, −2) **c** (3, −2), (1, 2) **d** (3, 4), (−1, −4)

3 (2, 4) (−2, −4)

Chapter 11

Homework 11A

1 a i 10.30 pm **ii** 11.10 pm **iii** 12.00 pm **b i** 50 kph **ii** 75 kph **iii** 50 kph

2 a 20 km **b** 40 km **c** 60 kph **d** 100 kph **3**

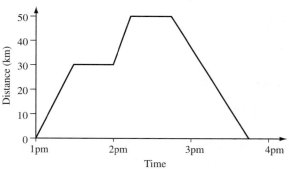

Homework 11B

1 a 2 **b** $\frac{1}{5}$ **c** −2 **d** $\frac{3}{2}$ **e** $\frac{1}{2}$ **f** $-\frac{3}{2}$ **g** 0 **h** $-\frac{4}{5}$ **i** $\frac{5}{2}$ **j** $-\frac{2}{5}$ **2 a** 17.5 kph **b** 30 mph

3 a 28.125 grams per ounce **b** 28.125 g

Homework 11C

1 a 20 m/s² **b** 0 m/s² **2 a** 3 m/s² **b** (−)2 m/s² **3 a**

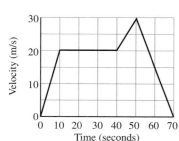

b (−)1.5 m/s²

4 a 50 mph **b** 30 minutes **c** straight line from (1100, 90) to (1230, 0) **d** 53 miles

Homework 11D

1 100.00 207.00 321.49 443.99 575.07 715.33 865.40 1025.98 1197.80 1381.64

2

pay back	owed
	£1000.00
£50.00	£1030.00
£75.00	£1037.40
£100.00	£1020.39
£125.00	£977.02
£150.00	£905.19
£175.00	£802.60
£200.00	£666.81
£225.00	£495.15
£250.00	£284.76
£275.00	£32.55

3 a 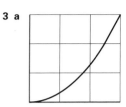 **b**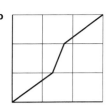

c 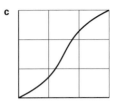 **d**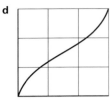

4 a Graph 1 = situation D Graph 2 = situation C Graph 3 = situation A Graph 4 = situation E

b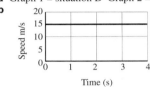

Chapter 12

Homework 12A

1 $x \times 3.5, y \times 3$; 2.5 **2 a** two sides in same ratio, included angle same. **b** $2:3$ **c** Q **d** CA **3 a** 4.8 **b** 4.88

Homework 12B

1 a 9.6 **b** $1\frac{8}{9}$ **2 a** $x = 6.875, y = 3.375$ **b** $x = 12, y = 12.5$ **3** 3.69 m **4** 7.2 metres

Homework 12C

1 $\frac{4}{3}$ **2** $\frac{5}{3}$ **3** 6 **4** 20 **5** $x = 5, y = 7$ **6** $x = 11.25, y = 6$ **7** $x = 20, y = 20.4$ **8** $x = 5, y = 7$

Homework 12D

1 a $9:49$ **b** $27:243$ **2**

Linear scale factor	Linear ratio	Linear fraction	Area scale factor	Volume scale factor
4	$1:4$	$\frac{4}{1}$	16	64
$\frac{1}{2}$	$2:1$	$\frac{1}{2}$	$\frac{1}{4}$	$\frac{1}{8}$
$\frac{1}{10}$	$10:1$	$\frac{1}{10}$	$\frac{1}{100}$	$\frac{1}{1000}$
6	$1:6$	$\frac{6}{1}$	36	216
5	$1:5$	$\frac{5}{1}$	25	125

3 320 cm^2 **4 a** 10 800 cm^3 **b** 50 000 cm^3 **5** 78.125 litres **6** 12.15 m^3 **7** 15, 36, 39 **8** $27x$ cm^3 **9 a** $2a$ **b** $8a^3$
10 a 5 cm **b** 0.012 litres **c** 2000 cm^2

Homework 12E

1 24.5 by 36.7 cm, 28.3 by 42.4 cm **2 a** 13.8 cm, 25.2 cm **b** 63 cm^2, 30.1 cm^2 **3** 48 m^2 **4** 30 minutes **5** 0.25 kg
6 a 9 m^2 **b** 20 000 cm^2 **7** 36 cm^2 **8** 76.8 cm^3

Chapter 13

Homework 13A

1 a 8.7 cm **b** 9.21 cm **c** 5.67 cm **2 a** 19.4 m **b** 33° **3 a** 49.3 km **b** 74.6 km **c** 146.5° **d** 89.4 km
4 a 17° **b** 63.44 m **c** 29.6 m **d** 27.5 m

Homework 13B

1 a 63.1° **b** 22.3 cm **c** 1902.4 cm^3 **d** 70.3° **2 a** 25.1° **b** 53.1°
3 a 6.7 cm **b** 33.9° **c** 14.4° **d** 10.54 cm **e** 8.2° **4 a i** 6.93 cm **ii** 9.16 cm **b** 62.4° **c** 23.9 cm

Homework 13C

1 23.6°, 156.4° **2** 26.7°, 153.3° **3** 40.5°, 139.5° **4** 15.7°, 164.3° **5** 26.9°, 153.1° **6** 203.6°, 336.4°
7 188.6°, 351.4° **8** 211.3°, 328.7° **9** 30°, 150° **10 i** 0.643 **ii** −0.643 **iii** 0.643 **iv** −0.643 **11** 221.8°, 318.2°

Homework 13D

1 45.6°, 314.4° **2** 67.7°, 292.3° **3** 51.9°, 308.1° **4** 67.9°, 292.1° **5** 85.1°, 274.9° **6** 126.9°, 233.1°
7 116.7°, 243.3° **8** 102.9°, 257.1° **9** 109.5°, 250.5° **10 i** −0.643 **ii** 0.643 **iii** 0.643 **iv** −0.643
11 99.6°, 260.4°

Homework 13E

1 a 0.454 **b** 0.454 **c** −0.454 **d** −0.454 **2 a** 0.358 **b** −0.358 **c** −0.358 **d** 0.358
3 same values different signs
4 a 23.6°, 156.4°, 203.6°, 336.4° **b** 60°, 120°, 240°, 300° **5 a** 90° **b** 109.5°, 250.5° **6** 50° and 130°

Homework 13F

1 27.8°, 207.8° **2** 38.7°, 218.7° **3** 53.5°, 233.5° **4** 72.8°, 252.8° **5** 111.4°, 291.4° **6** 171°, 351° **7** 141.8°, 321.8°
8 296.6°, 116.6° **9** 123.7°, 303.7° **10 i** −2.05 **ii** −2.05 **iii** 2.05 **iv** 2.05 **11** 63.4°, 243.4°

Homework 13G

1 a 4.42 m **b** 9.96 cm **2 a** 29.7° **b** 59.0° **3** 66.7°, 113.3° **4** 16.63 cm, 4.56 cm **5 a** 47° **b** 88 m **c** 131.9 m
6 64.95 m **7** 54.2 m

Homework 13H

1 a 9.54 m **b** 53.94 cm **2 a** 102.6° **b** 114.6° **3** 66.2° **4** 22.3°
5 a 11.86 cm **b** 37.7° **c** 27.3° **d** 5.63 cm **e** 54.4 cm^2 **6 a** 16.16 km **b** 035°

Homework 13I

1 a 8.6 m **b** 90° **c** 41° **d** 8.2 m **e** 90° **f** 866 cm **2** 16.44 cm **3 a** 66.8° **b** 9.4 cm **4** 7 cm

Homework 13J

1 $\dfrac{\sqrt{7}}{4}$ **2** 45° **3** $\dfrac{\sqrt{3}a^2}{4}$ cm^2 **4** 25 cm^2 **5 a** 4 cm **b** $\dfrac{\sqrt{6}}{4}, \dfrac{\sqrt{10}}{4}$

Homework 13K

1 a 37.34 cm^2 **b** 9.74 cm^2 **2** 4.54 cm **3** 48.25 cm^2 **4 a** 42.8° **b** 21° **5** 533.3 cm^2 **6** 15 cm^2

Chapter 14

Homework 14A

1 a $y = x + 2$ **b** $y = 3x − 1$ **c** $5y = 2x + 4$
2 a i $y = x$, $y = −x$ **ii** reflection in x- and y-axes **b i** $y = \frac{1}{2}x + 2$, $y = −\frac{1}{2}x + 2$ **ii** reflection in y-axis and $y = 2$
c i $2y = 5x + 3$, $2y = −5x + 13$ **ii** reflection in $x = 1$ and $y = 4$
3 $y = 2x + 4$, $y = 2x − 6$, $y = −\frac{1}{2}x + 4$, $y = −\frac{1}{2}x + \frac{3}{2}$

Homework 14B

2 a

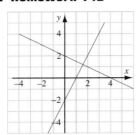

b $x = 1.6, y = 1.2$ **3 a**

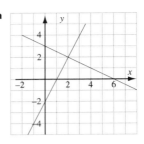

b $x = 2, y = 2$

Homework 14C

1 a £4   **b** 0.059   **c** C = 0.059x units + 4   **2 a** £10   **b** 0.02   **c** C = 0.02x units + 10
3 a £25   **b** 0.047   **c** C = 0.047x units + 25

Homework 14D

1 (5, −1)   **2** (3, 7)   **3** (−1, 3)   **4** Parallel   **5** (4, −2)   **6** (1.5, 6.5)   **7** (−3, 8)   **8** (−1, 5)   **9** (−3, 3)   **10** (−2, 4)
11 (2.5, 3.5)   **12** (3.5, −1.5)

Homework 14E

1 a

x	−3	−2	−1	0	1	2	3
$y = 2x^2$	18	8	2	0	2	8	18

b $y = 4$,   **c** ±2.2

2 a

x	−5	−4	−3	−2	−1	0	1	2	3	4	5
$y = x^2 + 3$	28	19	12	7	4	3	4	7	12	19	28

b 9.2,   **c** ±2.6

3 a

x	−3	−2	−1	0	1	2	3	4
$y = x^2 − 3x + 2$	20	12	6	2	0	0	2	6

b 8.75,   **c** −0.15, 3.15

Homework 14F

1 a

x	−1	0	1	2	3	4	5
$y = x^2 − 3x + 2$	6	2	0	0	1	6	12

b 1, 2

2 a

x	−1	0	1	2	3	4	5	6
$y = x^2 − 5x + 4$	10	4	0	−2	−2	0	4	10

b 1, 4

3 a

x	−5	−4	−3	−2	−1	0	1	2
$y = x^2 + 4x − 6$	−1	−6	−9	−10	−9	−6	−1	6

b 1.15, −5.15

Homework 14G

1 a

x	−12	−6	−4	−3	−2	−1	1	2	3	4	6	12
$y = \dfrac{12}{x}$	−1	−2	−3	−4	−6	−12	12	6	4	3	2	1

b i 8   **ii** 2.2

2 a

x	−8	−5	−4	−2	−1	1	2	4	5	8
$y = \dfrac{8}{x}$	−1	−1.6	−2	−4	−8	8	4	2	1.6	1

b i 2.3   **ii** 1.6

3 a

x	1	2	5	10	25	50
$y = \dfrac{50}{x}$	50	25	10	5	2	1

c 1.65

Homework 14H

1 a

x	–3	–2	–1	0	1	2	3
$y = x^3 + 1$	–26	–7	0	1	2	9	28

b 2.7

2 a

x	–2	–1	0	1	2	3
$y = x^3 + 2x$	–12	–3	0	3	12	33

b 20.6.

3 b 2.6.

Homework 14 I

1 a

x	–3	–2	–1	0	1	2	3	4
$y = 2^x$	0.1	0.3	0.5	1	2	4	8	16

c 5.7 **d** –0.4

2 a

x	–3	–2	–1	0	1	2	3
$y = (\frac{1}{3})^x$	27	9	3	1	0.3	0.1	0.04

c 0.06 **d** 0.25

3 c

Year	2	4	6	8	10	12	14	16	18	20
Total	3	15	63	255	1023	4095	16 000	65 000	260 000	1050 000

e Bert, eventually

Homework 14J

1 a –1.2, 3.2 **b** 4, –2 **c** 3, –1 **2 a** 2.6, 0.4 **b** 3.4, 0.6 **c** $y = x – 2$, 3, 1
3 a i –1.9 **ii** 1.4, –1.4, 0 **b** $y = x + 1$, –2, 1
4 a i –1.9, –0.3, 2.1 **ii** 1.7, 0.5, –2.2 **b** $y = x$, –2.1, –0.2, 2.3 **5 a** 1.7, 0.5 **b** 1.5, 0.3, –1.9

Chapter 15

Homework 15A

1 a

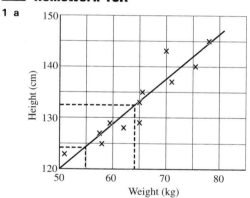

c 64 kg **d** 124 cm

2 a

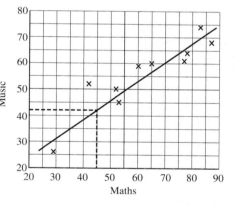

c Irene
d 42
e 95

Homework 15B

1 a

Time (seconds)	Number of runners	
$200 < x \le 240$	3	3
$240 < x \le 260$	7	10
$260 < x \le 280$	12	22
$280 < x \le 300$	23	45
$300 < x \le 320$	7	52
$320 < x \le 340$	5	57
$340 < x \le 360$	5	62

b

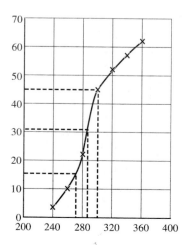

c Median = 283,
IQR = 30

2 a

Number of visits	Number of pages	
$0 < x \le 50$	6	6
$50 < x \le 100$	9	15
$100 < x \le 150$	15	30
$150 < x \le 200$	25	55
$200 < x \le 250$	31	86
$250 < x \le 300$	37	123
$300 < x \le 350$	32	155
$350 < x \le 400$	17	172
$400 < x \le 450$	5	177

b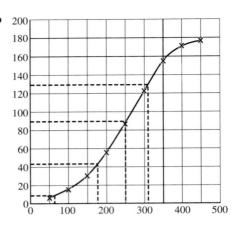

c Median = 250, IQR = 135   **d** 7 pages

Homework 15C

1 a

Peas per pod

b Distributions similar is shape but the older gardener has about 2.2 peas more per pod.

2 a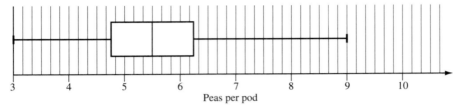

Monthly salary (£s)

b Men's distribution is very compact. Women's is more spread out and women generally get paid less than men.

3 a The flying bug batteries have a slightly higher median but are very inconsistent. The Ever Steady are very consistent.

b Ever Steady because they are very reliable.

4 a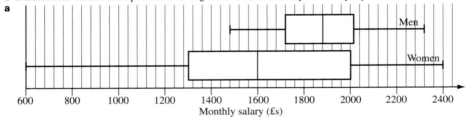

Time taken (minutes)

b Jack has lower median and a more consistent distribution.

c Jill because she takes too long on the phone.

5 a 57   **b**

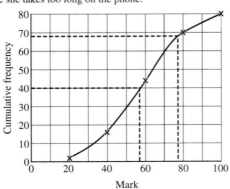

Mark

c i 58   **ii** 74

d Second school has about the same median but a much more compact and symmetrical distribution.

Homework 15D

1 a Mean 7.6, SD 2.24,   **b** 21.6, 3.77   **c** 87.2, 3.43   **d** 203, 1.41   **e** 72, 4.53   **f** 1, 3.63   **g** 97.2, 5.19   **h** 36.2, 5.01
2 a 12, 4.123   **b** 22, 4.123   **c** 120, 41.23   **3** 12, 16
4 a Salford, Mean 19 m 45.2 s SD 9.48 s, Bingley 19 m 53.8 s, 20.63, Sunderland 20 m 15 s, 30.25 s.
   b Salford, because they are fastest and most consistent.

Homework 15E

1 Mean 5.35, SD 2.13   **2 a** Mean 2, SD 1.17   **b** 124.3, 1.51   **c** 102, 1.17
3 a Class 1 Mean 5, SD 2.24   Class 2 5, 1.51   **b** Class 2 , lower SD more consistent
4 a Mean 90.16 SD 7.24   **b** She will be late on more than 15 days so not a good idea.

Chapter 16

Homework 16A

1 a 0.2 0.3 0.36 0.42 0.384   **b** 0.4   **c** 2000
2 a 0.16 0.253 0.141 0.17 0.103 0.168   **b** 100   **c** No, 2 occurs too often
3 a   **b** 13 red, 25 white and 12 blue

Red	White	Blue
0.31	0.52	0.17
0.272	0.48	0.248
0.255	0.508	0.238
0.254	0.504	0.242

4 a C   **b** A   **c** C   **d** A   **e** B   **f** A   **g** B   **5 a i** 0.2   **ii** 0.7   **iii** 0.6   **b** 10

Homework 16B

1 a $\frac{1}{6}$ **b** $\frac{1}{2}$ **c** $\frac{1}{13}$ **d** $\frac{1}{4}$ **e** $\frac{1}{3}$ **2 a** $\frac{1}{2}$ **b** $\frac{1}{3}$ **c** $\frac{1}{2}$ **d** $\frac{3}{52}$ **3 a** $\frac{1}{2}$ **b** $\frac{1}{3}$ **c** $\frac{5}{6}$ **4** $\frac{1}{160}$
5 a AB, AC, AD, AE, AF, BC, BD, BE, BF, CD, CE, CF, DE, DF, EF   **b** 1   **c** $\frac{1}{15}$ **d** 8   **e** $\frac{8}{15}$ **f** $\frac{2}{5}$
6 a $\frac{5}{12}$ **b i** 4   **ii** 7   **c i** $\frac{4}{11}$ **ii** $\frac{7}{11}$ **7 a** $\frac{1}{6}$ **b** $\frac{2}{3}$ **c** $\frac{5}{6}$ **d** 0   **e** 1
8 a $\frac{1}{3}$ **b** $\frac{1}{2}$ **c** $\frac{1}{4}$ **d** $\frac{1}{3}$ **e** $\frac{7}{12}$ **f** $\frac{3}{4}$ **9 a** $\frac{9}{40}$ **b** $\frac{3}{5}$

Homework 16C

1 a Yes   **b** Yes   **c** Yes   **d** No   **e** No   **2** b
3 a i $\frac{4}{11}$ **ii** $\frac{2}{11}$ **iii** $\frac{4}{11}$ **b i** Yes   **ii** Yes   **iii** Yes   **c** iii
4 a Ann, Joan,   Ann, Jack   Ann, John,   Ann, Arthur,   Ann, Ethel   Joan, Jack,   Joan, John,   Joan, Arthur,
   Joan, Ethel,   Jack, John,   Jack, Arthur,   Jack, Ethel   John, Arthur,   John, Ethel   Arthur, Ethel
   b i $\frac{1}{5}$ **ii** $\frac{1}{5}$ **iii** $\frac{4}{15}$ **iv** $\frac{11}{15}$ **c i** iii iv   **d** ii
5 $\frac{1}{6}$ **6 a** i, iv, v   **b** i   **7** May be windy and rainy. Windy and rainy are not independent events.

Homework 16D

1 100   **2** 250   **3 a** 52   **b** 8   **c** 4   **d** 2   **4** 21   **5** 1667   **6 a** 100   **b** 100   **c** 130   **d** 0   **7** 120
8 a You cannot add probabilities for events like this.   **b** Increase as he is more experienced
9 a 28 000   **b** 90% of 112 is 100.8 out of 200 so they should win.

Homework 16E

1 a $\frac{1}{2}$ **b** $\frac{1}{6}$ **c** $\frac{2}{3}$ **2 a** $\frac{1}{2}$ **b** $\frac{1}{2}$ **c** 1   **3 a** $\frac{1}{13}$ **b** $\frac{1}{13}$ **c** $\frac{2}{13}$ **4 a** $\frac{3}{10}$ **b** $\frac{3}{10}$ **c** $\frac{3}{5}$
5 a $\frac{1}{3}$ **b** $\frac{2}{3}$ **c** $\frac{11}{15}$ **d** $\frac{11}{15}$ **e** $\frac{1}{3}$ **6 a** 0.75   **b** 0.6   **c** 0.25   **d** 0.6   **e i** because 2 and red overlap   **ii** 0.5
7 a $\frac{3}{5}$ **b** $\frac{4}{5}$ **c** $\frac{3}{5}$ **8 a** 3   **b** not certain he has 3 double yolks to start with   **9 a** $\frac{11}{15}$ **b** $\frac{2}{3}$ **c** 0   **d** $\frac{2}{3}$

Homework 16F

1 (See diagram on page 437 of main pupil book)   **a i** $\frac{1}{6}$ **ii** $\frac{1}{4}$ **iii** $\frac{1}{6}$ **iv** $\frac{5}{36}$ **v** $\frac{1}{2}$ **vi** $\frac{29}{36}$
2 a $\frac{1}{6}$ **b** $\frac{11}{36}$ **c** $\frac{1}{9}$ **d** $\frac{3}{4}$ **e** $\frac{1}{36}$ **f** $\frac{11}{36}$ **g** $\frac{10}{36}$
3

Score on second dice						
6	−4	−2	0	2	4	6
5	−3	−1	1	3	5	7
4	−2	0	2	4	6	8
3	−1	1	3	5	7	9
2	0	2	4	6	8	10
1	1	3	5	7	9	11
	1	2	3	4	5	6

Score on first dice

a $\frac{1}{12}$ **b** $\frac{1}{6}$ **c** $\frac{1}{2}$ **d** $\frac{1}{6}$ **e** $\frac{13}{36}$
4 a $\frac{1}{2}$ **b** $\frac{1}{2}$ **c** $\frac{3}{4}$ **5 a** $\frac{1}{4}$ **b** $\frac{3}{8}$ **c** $\frac{7}{8}$ **6 a** $\frac{1}{12}$ **b** $\frac{1}{4}$
7 a DD, TD, HD, TT, HH, TH
b

Hyac	DH	DH	TH	HH
Tulip	DT	DT	TT	HT
Daff	DD	DD	TD	HD
Daff	DD	DD	TD	HD
	Daff	**Daff**	**Tulip**	**Hyac**

c $\frac{1}{4}$
d more daffodils

1

First event   Second event   Outcome   Probability

a $\frac{1}{36}$ **b** $\frac{10}{36}$ **c** $\frac{25}{36}$

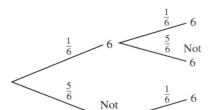

$\frac{1}{6}$ — 6   (6, 6) $\frac{1}{6} \times \frac{1}{6} = \frac{1}{36}$

$\frac{5}{6}$ Not 6   (6, Not 6) $\frac{1}{6} \times \frac{5}{6} = \frac{5}{36}$

$\frac{1}{6}$ — 6   (Not 6, 6) $\frac{5}{6} \times \frac{1}{6} = \frac{5}{36}$

$\frac{5}{6}$ Not 6   (Not 6, Not 6) $\frac{5}{6} \times \frac{5}{6} = \frac{25}{36}$

2 a $\frac{3}{5}$ **b**

First event   Second event   Outcome   Probability

c i $\frac{9}{25}$ **ii** $\frac{12}{25}$ **iii** $\frac{21}{25}$

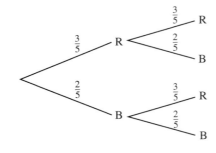

$\frac{3}{5}$ — R   (R, R) $\frac{3}{5} \times \frac{3}{5} = \frac{9}{25}$

$\frac{2}{5}$ — B   (R, B) $\frac{3}{5} \times \frac{2}{5} = \frac{6}{25}$

$\frac{3}{5}$ — R   (B, R) $\frac{2}{5} \times \frac{3}{5} = \frac{6}{25}$

$\frac{2}{5}$ — B   (B, B) $\frac{2}{5} \times \frac{2}{5} = \frac{4}{25}$

3

First event   Second event   Outcome   Probability

a $\frac{1}{4}$ **b** $\frac{3}{4}$ **c i** $\frac{1}{16}$ **ii** $\frac{7}{16}$

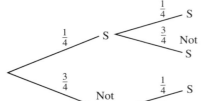

$\frac{1}{4}$ — S   (S, S) $\frac{1}{4} \times \frac{1}{4} = \frac{1}{16}$

$\frac{3}{4}$ Not S   (S, Not S) $\frac{1}{4} \times \frac{3}{4} = \frac{3}{16}$

$\frac{1}{4}$ — S   (Not S, S) $\frac{3}{4} \times \frac{1}{4} = \frac{3}{16}$

$\frac{3}{4}$ Not S   (Not S, Not S) $\frac{3}{4} \times \frac{3}{4} = \frac{9}{16}$

4 a i $\frac{5}{9}$ **ii** $\frac{4}{9}$ **b i** 8 **ii** 4 **c i** 8 **ii** 3

d First choice   Second choice   Outcome   Probability

e i $\frac{4}{9}$ **ii** $\frac{5}{6}$

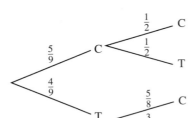

$\frac{1}{2}$ — C   (C, C) $\frac{5}{9} \times \frac{1}{2} = \frac{5}{18}$

$\frac{1}{2}$ — T   (C, T) $\frac{5}{9} \times \frac{1}{2} = \frac{5}{18}$

$\frac{5}{8}$ — C   (T, C) $\frac{4}{9} \times \frac{5}{8} = \frac{5}{18}$

$\frac{3}{8}$ — T   (T, T) $\frac{4}{9} \times \frac{3}{8} = \frac{1}{6}$

5 0.2

6 a $\frac{1}{3}$ **b**

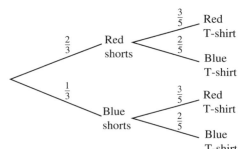

| First event | Second event | Outcome | Probability |

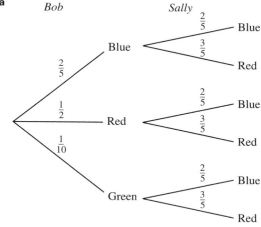

$\frac{3}{5}$ Red T-shirt $\quad$ (Red, Red) $\quad \frac{2}{3} \times \frac{3}{5} = \frac{2}{5}$

$\frac{2}{5}$ Blue T-shirt $\quad$ (Red, Blue) $\quad \frac{2}{3} \times \frac{2}{5} = \frac{4}{15}$

$\frac{3}{5}$ Red T-shirt $\quad$ (Blue, Red) $\quad \frac{1}{3} \times \frac{3}{5} = \frac{1}{5}$

$\frac{2}{5}$ Blue T-shirt $\quad$ (Blue, Blue) $\quad \frac{1}{3} \times \frac{2}{5} = \frac{2}{15}$

c i $\frac{8}{15}$
ii $\frac{7}{15}$
iii $\frac{13}{15}$

7 a

Bob $\quad$ Sally

$\frac{2}{5}$ Blue

$\frac{2}{5}$ Blue
$\frac{3}{5}$ Red

$\frac{1}{2}$ Red

$\frac{2}{5}$ Blue
$\frac{3}{5}$ Red

$\frac{1}{10}$ Green

$\frac{2}{5}$ Blue
$\frac{3}{5}$ Red

b 0.16 $\quad$ **c** 0.54

▄▄▄ Homework 16H

1 a $\frac{1}{16}$ **b** $\frac{3}{8}$ **2 a** $\frac{1}{16}$ **b** $\frac{1}{8}$ **3 a** $\frac{1}{17}$ **b** $\frac{13}{102}$ **4** $\frac{1}{54}$ **5 a** $\frac{9}{100}$ **b** $\frac{21}{50}$ **6 a** $\frac{1}{15}$ **b** $\frac{7}{15}$ **7 a** $\frac{1}{6}$ **b** $\frac{1}{36}$ **c** $\frac{13}{36}$

▄▄▄ Homework 16 I

1 a $\frac{243}{1024}$ **b** $\frac{781}{1024}$ **2 a** $\frac{1}{8}$ **b** $\frac{7}{8}$ **3 a** $\frac{1}{40}$ **b** $\frac{39}{40}$ **4 a** $\frac{49}{100}$ **b** $\frac{9}{100}$ **c** $\frac{91}{100}$ **5 a** $\frac{7}{15}$ **b** $\frac{1}{15}$ **c** $\frac{14}{15}$
6 a i $\frac{1}{8}$ **ii** $\frac{1}{8}$ **iii** $\frac{7}{8}$ **b i** $\frac{1}{16}$ **ii** $\frac{1}{16}$ **iii** $\frac{15}{16}$ **c i** $\frac{1}{32}$ **ii** $\frac{1}{32}$ **iii** $\frac{31}{32}$ **d i** $\frac{1}{2^n}$ **ii** $\frac{1}{2^n}$ **iii** $\frac{2^n - 1}{2^n}$
7 a $\frac{7}{50}$ **b** $\frac{43}{50}$ **8 a** $\frac{3}{5}$ **b** $\frac{3}{10}$ **c** $\frac{7}{10}$

▄▄▄ Homework 16J

1 a $\frac{8}{343}$ **b** $\frac{60}{343}$ **c** $\frac{150}{343}$ **d** $\frac{125}{343}$ **2 a** 0 **b** $\frac{1}{7}$ **c** $\frac{4}{7}$ **d** $\frac{2}{7}$ **3 a** 0 **b** $\frac{125}{216}$ **c** $\frac{75}{216}$ **4 a** 0.358 **b** 0.432
5 a 0.555 75 **b** 0.390 25 **c** 0.946 **6 a** 0.6 **b** 0.432 **c** large population **7 a** $\frac{7}{145}$ **b** $\frac{7}{15}$ **c** $\frac{27}{58}$

▄▄▄ Homework 16K

1 a i $\frac{1}{2}$ **ii** $\frac{1}{2}$ **b i** $\frac{4}{7}$ **ii** $\frac{3}{7}$ **2 a i** $\frac{14}{33}$ **ii** $\frac{1}{11}$ **b** $\frac{28}{165}$ **c** $\frac{56}{495}$ **d** 1
3 a $\frac{1}{6}$ **b** $\frac{1}{2}$ **c** $\frac{3}{10}$ **d** $\frac{1}{30}$ **4 a** $\frac{3}{8}$ **b** $\frac{1}{6}$ **c** $\frac{11}{24}$ **d** $\frac{5}{6}$ **5 a** $\frac{33}{66640}$ **b** $\frac{33}{16660}$ **c** $\frac{1}{270725}$ **d** $\frac{1}{20825}$ **6 a** $\frac{1}{2}$ **b** 12.5

▄▄▄ Homework 16L

1 a i $\frac{125}{512}$ **ii** $\frac{485}{512}$ **b i** $\frac{5}{28}$ **ii** $\frac{55}{56}$ **2** $\frac{7}{16}$ **3** $\frac{15}{16}$ **4 a** $\frac{57}{980}$ **b** $\frac{923}{980}$ **5** $\frac{319}{490}$
6 a $\frac{1}{16}$ **b** $\frac{3}{4}$ **7 a** $\frac{8}{27}$ **b** $\frac{4}{9}$ **c** $\frac{1727}{1728}$ **8 a** 0.856 52 **b** 0.993 56
9 a $\frac{2}{3}$ **b i** 0.010 24 **ii** 0.2592 **iii** 0.077 76 **iv** 0.922 24 **10 a** $\frac{1}{5}$ **b** $\frac{1}{5}$
11 a $\frac{2}{5}$ **b** $\frac{1}{15}$ **c** $\frac{7}{15}$ **d** $\frac{14}{15}$ **12 a** $\frac{1}{59049}$ **b** $\frac{32768}{59049}$ **c** $\frac{26281}{59049}$
13 a $(\frac{2}{3})^3$ **b** $3 \times (\frac{2}{3})^2 \times (\frac{1}{3})$ **c** 2 **14 a** $\frac{10}{21}$ **b i** 83 **ii** $\frac{3}{9} \times \frac{2}{8} \approx 0.083$

Chapter 17

▄▄▄ Homework 17A

1 a 4, 7, 10, 13, 16 **b** 1, 3, 5, 7, 9 **c** 6, 10, 14, 18, 22 **d** 2, 8, 18, 32, 50 **e** 0, 3, 8, 15, 24
2 a 3, 4, 5, 6, 7 **b** 3, 7, 11, 15, 19 **c** 1, 5, 9, 13, 17 **d** 2, 5, 10, 17, 26 **e** 3, 9, 19, 33, 51

3 a $\frac{3}{2}, \frac{5}{3}, \frac{7}{4}, \frac{9}{5}, \frac{11}{6}, \frac{13}{7}$ **b** 1.999 **c** 2 **4 a i** $\frac{11}{12}$ **ii** $\frac{n}{n + 1}$ **b** 2, $\frac{3}{2}, \frac{4}{3}, \frac{5}{4}$

Homework 17B

1 a $2n+3$ **b** $4n-1$ **c** $5n+1$ **d** $6n-3$ **e** $3n+1$ **f** $7n-4$
2 a 101 **b** 201 **c** 253 **d** 296 **e** 152 **f** 345
3 a i $3n+1$ **ii** 301 **iii** 100 **b i** $2n+5$ **ii** 205 **iii** 99, 101 **c i** $5n-2$ **ii** 498 **iii** 98
  d i $4n-3$ **ii** 397 **iii** 101 **e i** $8n-6$ **ii** 794 **iii** 98 **f i** $n+4$ **ii** 104 **iii** 100

4 a $\dfrac{2n+1}{3n+2}$ **b** 0.6, 0.625, 0.636, 0.643 **c i** 0.6656 **ii** 0.667 **d** 0.667

5 a i 13 **ii** by adding the 8th and 9th terms **b** $4n-3$

Homework 17C

1 a  **b** $5n+1$ **c** 126 **d** 39th
2 a 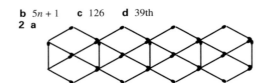 **b** $9n+1$ **c** 541 **d** 11th

3 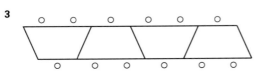 **a** 12 **b** $3n$ **c** 17
4 a 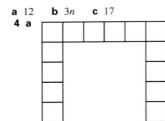 **b** $3n+2$ **c** 152 **d** 99

5 a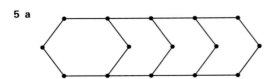

b

Number of enclosures	1	2	3	4	5	6	7	8
Number of posts	6	9	12	15	18	21	24	27

c 63 **d** $3n+3$

Homework 17D

1 a i 36, 49 **ii** n^2 **b i** 37, 50 **ii** n^2+1 **c i** 40, 53 **ii** n^2+4 **d i** 72, 98 **ii** $2n^2$ **e i** 56, 69 **ii** n^2+20
2 a i 40, 54 **ii** $n(n+3)$ **b i** 63, 80 **ii** $(n+2)(n+4)$ **c i** 30, 42 **ii** $n(n+1)$ **d i** 15, 21 **ii** $\frac{1}{2}n(n+1)$
  e i 42, 56 **ii** $(n+1)(n+2)$
3 a i n^2+2n+5 **ii** 2605 **b i** $3n+5$ **ii** 155 **c i** $(n+1)(n+3)$ **ii** 2703 **d i** $(n-1)(n+3)$ **ii** 2597
4 a i 14 **b i** 57 **ii** add on 3 more each time

Homework 17E

1 $\dfrac{-5y}{2}$ **2** $\dfrac{(p+q)b}{p-q}$ **3** $\dfrac{a}{2b^2+c}$ **4** $\dfrac{s(t+1)-3}{2}$ **5** $\dfrac{3r}{s+3}$ **6 a** $\dfrac{b}{a+c}$ **b** $\dfrac{b}{a-b-1}$ **c** $\dfrac{2a}{b+d}$ **d** $\dfrac{cd}{2c-d}$

7 a $\dfrac{p}{2\pi+4}$ **b** $\sqrt{\dfrac{A}{\pi+4}}$ **8 a** $\dfrac{2-3y}{y-1}$ **b** $\dfrac{2+y}{y+3}$ **9** $\dfrac{2}{b-5}$ **10 a** $\dfrac{aR}{a-R}$ **b** $\dfrac{bR}{b-R}$

Chapter 18

Homework 18A

1 $3a+b$ **2** $6x$ **3** $5p$ **4** $2r+2\pi r$ **5** $2R+\pi R$ **6** $3q+2p$ **7** $\pi(a+b)$

Homework 18B

1 $\frac{1}{2}bh$ **2** $2ab$ **3** $\frac{1}{2}\pi r^2+\frac{1}{2}\pi R^2+a(R+r)$ **4** $d^2+\dfrac{\pi d^2}{2}$ **5** $bk+\frac{1}{2}h(a+b)$ **6** x^2-y^2 **7** $\pi h(a+b)$

■ Homework 18C

1 x^3 **2** $2\pi r^3$ **3** $x(x^2 - y^2)$ **4** $a^2 b$ **5** $\pi(R^2 - r^2)h$ **6** $abc + a^2 c$ **7 a** Volume **b** Perimeter **c** Area

■ Homework 18D

1 a L **b** A **c** V **d** N **e** L **f** A **g** N **h** V **i** N **j** N
2 a A **b** V **c** V **d** V **e** A **f** V **g** L **h** V **3 a** represents a length **b ii** it is Length × length = area

■ Homework 18E

1 a C **b** I **c** I **d** I **e** I **f** C **g** I **h** C
2 a C,A **b** C,L **c** I, **d** C,L **e** C,V **f** I **g** C,A **h** C,N **3 a** 2 **b** 1 **c** 2 **d** 2
4 a V **b** V **c** L **d** L **e** None

Chapter 19

■ Homework 19A

1 a 24 **b** 12.5 **2 a** 72 **b** 5 **3 a** 125 **b** 6 **4 a** 72 **b** 2 **5 a** 120 **b** 7.5 **6 a** 180 **b** 7
7 a £24 **b** 48 l **8 a** 38 **b** 96 m^2 **9** 3 hrs 45 mins

■ Homework 19B

1 a 250 **b** 6.32 **2 a** 6.4 **b** 12.6 **3 a** 150 **b** 1.414 **4 a** 70 **b** 256 **5 a** 200 **b** 5.76
6 a 12.74 **b** 55.4 **7 a** 256 **b** 2.32 **8 a** 7.5° **b** 10.4 atm **9 a** 80 g **b** 4
10 a 125 J **b** 14.14 m/s **11** 31.6 km

■ Homework 19C

1 a 5.6 **b** 0.5 **2 a** 30 **b** 9 **3 a** 2.5 **b** 0.5 **4 a** 7.2 **b** 0.5 **5 a** 9.6 **b** 4096 **6 a** 71.6 **b** 4
7 20 **8 a** 1.25 **b** 2.5 **9 a** $y = \dfrac{192}{x^2}$ **b i** 5.33 **ii** 2.3

Chapter 20

■ Homework 20A

1 a 6.5–7.5 **b** 17.5–18.5 **c** 29.5–30.5 **d** 746.5–747.5 **e** 9.75–9.85 **f** 32.05–32.15 **g** 2.95–3.05
h 89.5–90.5 **i** 4.195–4.205 **j** 1.995–2.005 **k** 34.565–34.575 **l** 99.5–105
2 a 45.7 **b** 20 **c** 0.32

■ Homework 20B

1 a 5.5–6.5 **b** 33.5–34.5 **c** 55.5–56.5 **d** 79.5–80.5 **e** 3.695–3.705 **f** 0.85–0.95 **g** 0.075–0.085
h 895–905 **i** 0.695–0.705 **j** 359.5–360.5 **k** 16.5–17.5 **l** 195–205
2 a 15.5 **b** 14.5 **c** 310 **d** 290 **3 a** $41.75 \leq$ time 41.85 **b** 19.00 m/s **c** 71 mph

■ Homework 20C

1 a 18.75–29.75 **b** 20.0025–20.9625 **c** 147.477 625–147.744 025 **2 a** 7.5–8.5, 4.5–5.5 **b** 46.75 m^2 **c** 24 m
3 1401.75 – 1478.75 m^2 **4** 388.125 – 584.375 cm^2 **5** 16.12 – 17.23 **6 a** 13.67 – 18.66 **b** 4.97
7 a 12.25, 12.35 **b** 99.995, 100.005 **c** 8.164 m/s **8** 2.98, 3.02 **9** 24.93, 25.07 **10** 48.7°

Chapter 21

■ Homework 21A

1 a $x < 5$ **b** $t > 8$ **c** $p \geq 8$ **d** $x < 3$ **e** $y \leq 6$ **f** $t > 9$ **g** $x < 13$ **h** $y \leq 11$ **i** $t \geq 37$ **j** $x < 10$ **k** $x \leq 2$
l $t \geq \frac{7}{4}$ **m** $x \geq -6$ **n** $t \leq 4$ **o** $y \leq 6$ **p** $x \geq \frac{1}{2}$ **q** $w \leq 3.5$ **r** $x \leq \frac{5}{8}$
2 a 5, 4, 3, 2, 1 **b** no answer **c** 25, 16, 9, 4, 1 **d** 5, 3, 1 **e** 7, 5, 3, 2
3 a $2 < x < 3$ **b** $1 < x < 4$ **c** $-2 < x < 4$ **d** $2 \leq x < \frac{10}{3}$ **e** $3.5 \leq x < 7.5$ **f** $\frac{1}{2} \leq x < 3.75$ **g** $2 \leq x \leq 4$ **h** $\frac{5}{2} \leq x < 8$
i $\frac{4}{5} \leq x < 4.2$

Homework 21B

1 a $x \geq 1$　**b** $x < 2$　**c** $x > -2$　**d** $x \leq 0$　**e** $x > -5$　**f** $x \geq -1$

2

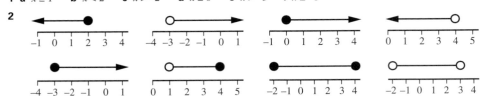

3 a $x \geq 4$　**b** $x < -2$　**c** $x \leq 5$　**d** $x > 3$　**e** $x \leq 1.5$　**f** $x \geq 4$　**g** $x > 7$　**h** $x < -1$　**i** $x < 2$　**j** $x \leq 3$　**k** $x > 24$
l $x \geq -2$
4 a $x > \frac{4}{5}$　**b** $x \leq 3$　**c** $x \geq \frac{19}{4}$　**d** $x < 6.5$　**e** $x \leq \frac{1}{2}$　**f** $x > -2$　**g** $x \geq -7$　**h** $x \leq -\frac{2}{5}$

Homework 21C

1 $-3 \leq x \leq 3$　**2** $x < -6, x > 6$　**3** $-10 < x < 10$　**4** $x \leq -2, x \geq 2$　**5** $x \leq -5, x \geq 5$　**6** $x < -4, x > 4$　**7** $-3 \leq x \leq 3$
8 All values　**9** $x < -1, x > 1$　**10** $x \leq -5, x \geq 5$　**11** $x < -4, x > 4$　**12** $-3 < x < 3$　**13** $-\sqrt{2.8} \leq x \leq \sqrt{2.8}$
14 $-\sqrt{16} < x < \sqrt{16}$　**15** $x \leq -5, x \geq 5$　**16** $x \leq -12, x \geq 12$　**17** $-0.4 < x < 0.4$　**18** $x \leq -1.1, x \geq 1.1$　**19** $-\sqrt{93} \leq x \leq \sqrt{93}$
20 $x < -0.5, x > 0.5$

Homework 21D

1

2

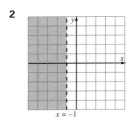

3

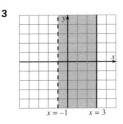

4

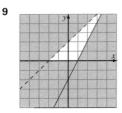

b i Yes　**ii** Yes　**iii** No　**iv** Yes

5

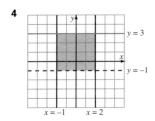

6

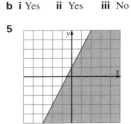

7

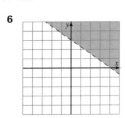

8

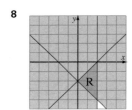

9

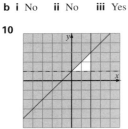

b i No　**ii** No　**iii** Yes　**iv** No

10

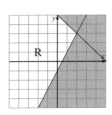

b (1, 2) (2, 2) (2, 3)

Homework 21E

1 a $6x$　**b** $20y$　**c** $6x + 20y$　**2 a** £1.75　**b** $50x + 75y$　**c** $350 - 50x$, No
3 a $Ax + By$　**b** $Ax + 3Bx$　**c** $Ax + Bx + 5B$　**4 a** May be　**b** may be　**c** May be
5 $60x + 75y < 600$. Cancel by 15
6 a time to read a book $3x + y < 14$ days. At least 3 novels, $x > 3$. No more than 7 books and magazines, $x + y < 7$
b i yes　**ii** no　**iii** no　**iv** no
7 number of seats $x + y \leq 200$　Money $2x + 3y \geq 450$　No more than twice £3 tickets to £2 tickets. $y \leq 2x$

Homework 21F

1 a cost of discs　**b** Space $100x + 250y \geq 4000$ Cancel by 50　**c i** no　**ii** no　**iii** no
2 a cost $60x + 40y \leq 300$. Cancel by 20　**b** peas $\geq$ beans + 2.　**c** (1, 3), (1, 4), (1, 5), (1, 6), (2, 4)
3 a $5x + 4y \leq 1000$　**b** Each hardback takes two spaces.　**c** $x + y \geq 175$
d Substitute into inequalities to show they are all true.　**e i** (64, 170)　**ii** (0, 200)　**iii** (0, 250)

4 a $4x + 5y \leq 70$ **b** $2x + y \leq 20$ **c** e.g. 8 donkeys and 4 horses.
5 a $5x + 6y \leq 120$ **b** $0.2x + 0.15y \leq 4$, multiply by 20 **c** $y > 2x$ **d i** no **ii** no **iii** yes
6 a $2x + y \leq 40$, $y \leq 2x$, **b** 30 **c** £260

Homework 21G

1 a 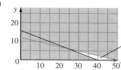 $6x + 25y \leq 300$, $2x + 5y \geq 80$ **b** $x = 25$, $y = 6$ **c** $x = 40$ **d** $x = 50$

2 a 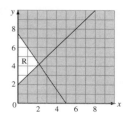 $3x + 2y \leq 15$, $y \geq x + 2$

b 2 tins of peas **c** 2 tins of beans, 4 tins of peas

3 a $x + y \geq 175$, $2x + y \leq 300$, $5x + 4y \leq 1000$

b i 250 paperbacks **ii** 125 paperbacks. 50 hardback **iii** 175 paperbacks

4 a 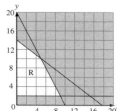 $h \geq 2$, $2d + 5h < 70$, $5d + h < 20$

b $d = 6$, $h = 8$
c $d = 0$, $h = 2$

5 a 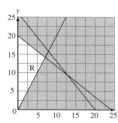 $5x + 6y \leq 120$, $y \geq 2x$, $4x + 3y \leq 80$

b 21 birds (7, 14) **c** No birds at all!

6 a 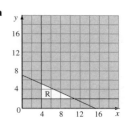 Time $4x + 8y \leq 60$ cancel by 4

b $x \geq 4$, $y \geq 2$ **c** 11 standard, 2 deluxe

7 a 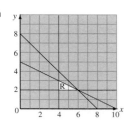 $x + 2y \leq 10$, $x + y < 8$, $x > 4$, $y > 2$

b 6 chips and 2 fish give £230.

8 b 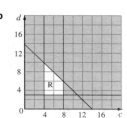 $c + d \leq 14$, $c \geq 4$, $c \leq 8$, $d \geq 3$

c 4 canoes and 7 dinghies cost £960, giving 11 boats.

Chapter 22

Homework 22A

1 a 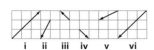 **b** Opposite **2 a**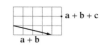

b Cancel each other out
c $a = \binom{2}{2}$ $b = \binom{2}{-3}$ $c \binom{-4}{1}$
i $\binom{0}{5}$ **ii** $\binom{6}{1}$ **iii** $\binom{0}{0}$

3 a i $\binom{2}{-1}$ **ii** $\binom{4}{-2}$ **iii** $\binom{2}{-1}$ **b** all parallel **c** Yes. Parallel with a common point.

4 a i $b - a$ **ii** $\frac{1}{2}(b - a)$ **iii** $\frac{1}{2}(a + b)$ **b** $XY = b - a$ **c** AB

5 a a, b $\binom{2}{1}$ **b** e.g. c, e $\binom{-2}{4}$ $\binom{2}{-4}$ same values different signs **c** e.g. c, d $\binom{-1}{2}$ $\binom{-2}{4}$ multiples of each other

d e.g. c, g $\binom{-2}{4}$ $\binom{-4}{2}$ opposite values in same ratio

6 a $\frac{3}{4}b$ **b** $\frac{2}{3}a$ **c** $\frac{1}{2}(a + b)$ **d** $\frac{1}{4}b - \frac{1}{2}a$ **e** $\frac{1}{2}b - \frac{1}{6}a$ **f** $-\frac{3}{4}b + \frac{2}{3}a$ **g** zero. Form a closed triangle
7 a $\frac{1}{2}b$ **b** $\frac{1}{4}a + \frac{1}{2}b$ **c** $\frac{3}{4}a$ **d** multiples **8 a** $\frac{3}{4}b + \frac{1}{4}a$ **b** $\frac{1}{4}a + \frac{2}{3}b$ **9 a** $5p - 10q$ **b** $4p - 8q$ **c** $2q + 4p$

▬ Homework 22B

1 a $\frac{1}{3}(a - b)$ **b** $\frac{1}{3}a + \frac{2}{3}b$ **c** $b + \frac{1}{2}a$ **d** straight line
2 a i $-a + \frac{1}{3}b$ **ii** $-b + \frac{2}{3}a$ **b** $OA + n(AP)$ **c** $OB + m(BQ)$ **e** $\frac{4}{7}a + \frac{1}{7}b$
3 a $\frac{1}{3}(a + b)$ **b** $b - \frac{1}{3}a$ **c** along OR and $OG = OQ + QG$ **d** $n = \frac{2}{3}$ and $m = \frac{1}{3}$ **e** $\frac{1}{3}a + \frac{1}{3}b$
4 a i $b - a$ **ii** $2b - 2a$ **b** parallel **5 a i** $-3p + 3q$ **ii** $-3p + 12q$ **b** $2p + 4q$ **c** straight line.
6 a i $c - b$ **ii** $\frac{1}{2}c$ **iii** $\frac{1}{2}c$ **b** parallelogram because $NQ = MP = \frac{1}{2}q$
7 a i $\frac{1}{2}b + a$ **ii** $-\frac{1}{2}b + a$ **iii** $a + b$ **b** $\frac{1}{2}(a + b)$ **c i** $-\frac{1}{3}a - \frac{1}{3}b$ **ii** $\frac{2}{3}a + \frac{1}{6}b$
d parallel in opposite directions and one is twice length of other.
8 a $b + r$ **b** $b - r$ **c** $\frac{1}{2}(a + b + r)$

Chapter 23

▬ Homework 23A

1 e i (**a** to **b**) stretch sf 2 in y-direction **ii** (**a** to **c**) translation $\binom{0}{2}$ **iii** (**a** to **d**) translation $\binom{-2}{0}$

2 e i stretch sf 3, translation $\binom{0}{2}$ **ii** translation $\binom{0}{-3}$ **iii** stretch sf $\frac{1}{2}$ in y-direction, translation $\binom{0}{1}$

3 e i translation $\binom{-4}{0}$ **ii** reflection in x-axis **iii** reflection in x-axis, translation $\binom{0}{2}$

4 e i stretch sf 3 in y-direction **ii** translation $\binom{0}{3}$ **iii** translation $\binom{-30}{0}$

5 e i reflection in x-axis **ii** stretch sf 3 in x-direction **iii** stretch sf 3 in y, stretch sf 2 in x

6 e i stretch sf 3 in y-direction **ii** translation $\binom{-45}{0}$ **iii** stretch sf 2 in y, translation $\binom{-90}{0}$

7 e i reflection in x-axis **ii** translation $\binom{0}{4}$ **iii** stretch sf 2 in y

8 e i stretch sf 3 in y-direction **ii** translation $\binom{-60}{0}$ **iii** stretch sf 2 in y, translation $\binom{0}{3}$

9 $\sin(x + 90)$ is translated by $\binom{-90}{0}$ to give $\cos x$

10 c translated by $\binom{2}{4}$

▬ Homework 23B

1 a $y = 3x^2$ **b** $y = x^2 + 2$ **c** $y = (x + 4)^2$ **d** $y = 2x^2 + 3$ **e** $y = (x + 3)^2 - 2$ **f** $y = -2x^2$
2 a $y = 2\sin x$ **b** $y = \sin x + 2$ **c** $y = \sin(x - 60) + 2$ **d** $y = \frac{1}{3}\sin x - 1$ **e** $y = \sin(x - 90) - 1$
3 a $y = x^2 + 3$ **b** $y = (x - 3)^2$ **c** $y = x^2$ **d** $y = -x^2 + 9$
4 a $y = 3\sin x$ **b** $y = \sin(x - 60)$ **c** $y = 2\sin(x - 30)$ **d** $y = 2\sin 2x$

5 a e.g. reflection in x-axis and translation of $\binom{-90}{0}$ **b i** equivalent **ii** equivalent **iii** not equivalent

6 a matches **i** **b** matches **v** **c** matches **iv** **d** matches **ii** **e** matches **iii**
7

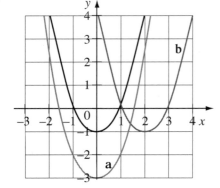